THE GOSPEL OF EVOLUTION

Ch. Darwin

1809—1882.

THE GOSPEL OF EVOLUTION

BY

PROFESSOR J. ARTHUR THOMSON

LONDON
GEORGE NEWNES LIMITED

PRINTED IN GREAT BRITAIN BY THE WHITEFRIARS PRESS LTD.,
LONDON AND TONBRIDGE.

PREFACE

THE leading idea of this unconventional little book is that the story of Organic Evolution has good news for Man. For millions of years there has been an advancement of life, not without its retrogressions and blind alleys, it is true, but on the whole progressive; not without disharmonies, we admit, yet, as Lotze said, " an onward-advancing melody,"a heartening music. There has been a gradual emergence of finer forms of life, a persistent victory of life over things, a growing emancipation of the Psyche. Organic Evolution means an emergence of lives that are increasingly satisfactions in themselves. Why should this stop? The momentum of Organic Evolution is with and in Man at his best.

J. ARTHUR THOMSON.

CONTENTS

THE GOSPEL OF EVOLUTION

I

WHAT EVOLUTION MEANS

EVOLUTION is too wide a word to be defined, for it is the process of BECOMING, but if we take it as an abbreviation of " Organic Evolution," it means that the plants and animals we see around us are derived by continuous natural change from predecessors slightly different, and on the whole rather simpler. It means that the present is the child of the past and the parent of the future. It is a word for the way in which living creatures, including mankind, have come to be as they are. Evolution is the process of Becoming when we think not of a particular individual, but of all the individuals—living and dead—that make up a race or a species. Biologists have almost quite agreed to use the word *development* when they speak of what Harvey called the minting and coining of the chick out of the egg, and to use the word *evolu-*

tion when they are speaking of the long-drawn-out process by which, let us say, the race of birds emerged from a dimly known ancestry among extinct reptiles, or the modern horses, stepping daintily on the tiptoe of a single digit (the third), arose from small progenitors with three or four fully developed toes reaching the ground.

FACT AND FACTORS.

But the idea of evolution does not commit one to any particular theory of the factors that were operative in bringing about the gradual transformation from one type to another. Many firmly convinced evolutionists are very chary of committing themselves to any particular theory of how the changes came about, such as the Lamarckian Theory or the Darwinian Theory. In ordinary conversation one might be asked : " Do you accept the Darwinian Theory ? " when all that was meant was : " Are you an evolutionist ? " The answer would, of course, be " Yes," for all competent biologists of to-day are evolutionists (see Chapter Three). But if the same question, " Do you accept the Darwinian theory ? " was asked among students of biology, it would mean : " Are you convinced as to the satisfactoriness of Darwin's theory of Nature's sifting of variations that crop up ? " To this question some would say " Yes," and others " No," and others " So far as it goes."

THE PICTURE LUCRETIUS DREW.

At the present time there is only one scientific picture of how living creatures may have come to be as they are, and that is the evolutionist picture. There is no rival scientific view. Nowadays it is not so much a theory as a necessary way of looking at things, and there is nowadays no alternative as long as we talk science.

But it was not always so. Thus the Roman poet Lucretius (99–55 B.C.), who was greatly interested in scientific questions, was an exponent of what might be called a theory of wholesale spontaneous generation. In Book V., 780, of his " De Rerum Natura," he says : " Plants and trees arise directly out of the earth in the same manner that feathers and hair grow from the bodies of animals. Living beings certainly have not fallen from heaven, nor, as Anaxagoras supposed, have land animals arisen from the sea. But as even now many animals, under the influence of rain and the heat of the sun, arise from the earth, so under the fresh, youthful, productive forces of the younger earth, they were spontaneously produced in larger numbers. In this manner were first produced birds, from the warmth of spring; then other animals sprang from the womb of the earth."

This seems a fantastic picture to us, but it is not devoid of beauty. It is one of the finest non-evolutionist pictures—how from the earth there sprang race after race of verdant herbs, tribe after tribe of sentient life, " by showers and sunshine ushered into day."

> " Of these birds first, of wing and plume diverse,
> Broke their light shells in springtime; as in spring
> Still breaks the grasshopper his curious web,
> And seeks, spontaneous, foods and vital air.

. . . . . .

> " Hence the dear name of mother, o'er and o'er,
> Earth claims most justly, since the race of man
> Long bore she of herself, each brutal tribe
> Wild-wandering o'er the mountains, and the birds
> Gay-winged, that cleave, diverse, the liquid air."

The earth still receives from many " the dear name of mother," but not even the dreamiest can think of animals making their first appearance out of the ground. The Daddy-Long-Legs that we see creeping out of the soil on a putting-green are developing, not evolving; they are coming out because they were previously, as eggs, put in.

MILTON'S PICTURE.

But the fantastic picture of animals as " earth-children" (so Lucretius called them), lasted for many centuries, and we must remember that the theory of the spontaneous generation of simple living creatures was still reasserting itself during the lifetime of Pasteur. And if a little creature may arise spontaneously and apart from antecedent life in a saucerful of mud, why not a largish animal from the womb of the earth ? But neither event ever happens !

Milton's picture of Becoming differs from that of Lucretius in definitely implying Creation. Lucretius thought of spontaneous generation in a naturalistic way, for just as he believed that insects and worms were in his own day made in the earth and out of the earth, so he supposed it had been in the past, only on a grander scale. But Milton thought of living creatures arising in a way beyond our understanding : they were created by God out of the dust of the earth. Science is always seeking after naturalistic description, accounting for results in terms of measurable materials and forces. Milton's picture was not scientific, nor meant to be.

> " The earth obeyed, and straight
> Op'ning her fertile womb, teemed at a birth
> Innumerous living creatures, perfect forms,
> Limbed and full grown. Out of the ground uprose,
> As from his lair, the wild beast, where he wons
> In forest wild, in thicket, brake or den :
> Among the trees they rose, they rose and walked ;

The cattle in the fields and meadows green :
Those rare and solitary, these in flocks
Pasturing at once, and in broad herds upsprung.
The grassy clods now calv'd ; now half appear'd
The tawny lion, pawing to get free
His hinder parts, then springs, as broken from bonds,
And rampant shakes his brindled mane."

CREATION AND EVOLUTION.

One should try to avoid looking at august
problems in a hard, wooden way. There may be
a great truth in the idea of creation, though
Milton's picture strikes one as rather ridiculous.
That great truth may be this :—

" In the beginning was Mind, and that Mind
was with God, and the Mind was God. The
same was in the beginning with God. All things
were made by it ; and without it was not anything made that was made. In it was life, and
the life was the light of men. And the light
shineth in the darkness and the darkness over-
powered it not. . . ."—St. John I., i—v.*

As long as the doctrine of Creation expresses a
religious truth like this, it is not for Science to
say a word. For Science has nothing to do with
religious interpretations ; it has only to do with
empirical descriptions.

But if those who believe that there is a great
truth expressed or hinted at in the opening

* "The Spirit of Man," Robert Bridges, 1916, No. 42.

verses of St. John's Gospel, go on to say, " Living creatures emerged from the earth just as we see them to-day," then the naturalist must answer firmly : " This is not in accordance with the facts of the case as shown in the rock-records." Or if the creationist says : " Well, well ! I am convinced that living creatures arose in some way entirely beyond scientific analysis," the naturalist must answer firmly : " It is far too soon to take up that position ; the way in which things came to be is becoming clearer every year ; man has no right to shirk his duty as scientific inquirer."

A SUCCESSION OF CREATIONS.

In the early days of the " evolution or creation " argument, a clever idea was suggested by some who could not see their way to accept the implications of Darwin's picture. It was the idea of " successive creations "—that each geological period had been the scene of a special creation, which was an advance on what had already taken place. Thus in the later Old Red Sandstone period, there was supposed to have been a creation of the first Amphibians, in the Permian a creation of the first Reptiles, in the Jurassic a creation of the first Birds, and so on. But if it is unsatisfactory, indeed illegitimate, to postulate one origin in a way that cannot be

B 2

scientifically understood, how much worse to have instalments of these origins all through the ages! One inexplicable emergence is bad enough, but scores of them! Moreover, the successive appearance of higher and higher types is a scientific fact, whereas creation is a religious or theological idea, and mixing the two always means confusion of thought. When the creationist says that behind all things and their history there is the Power of the Living God, he is beyond all scientific criticism, but when he passes into detailed description or denies the possibility of any, he is going beyond his *metier*.

ALFRED RUSSEL WALLACE'S TWO WORLDS.

One of the most picturesque figures among evolutionists was Alfred Russel Wallace (1822–1913), who shared with Darwin the credit of thinking out the theory of Natural Selection or Nature's Sifting. He was a naturalist in the old and truest sense, a great traveller, rich in a world-wide experience of animal life, a specialist on geographical distribution, and yet concerned with the most general problems of biology, a fearless thinker and a social reformer, a man of science whose eyes were always open to the spiritual aspect of the world.

We cannot too often admire magnanimity, so

we quote this stirring passage from Romanes, himself an evolutionist of distinction :—

" It was in the highest degree dramatic that the great idea of natural selection should have occurred independently and in precisely the same form to two working naturalists ; that these agreed to publish their theory on the same day ; and last, but not least, that through the many years of strife and turmoil which followed, these two English naturalists consistently maintained towards each other such feelings of magnanimous recognition that it is hard to say whether we should most admire the intellectual or the moral qualities which, in relation to their common labours, they have displayed."

"SPIRITUAL INFLUX."

Now, Alfred Russel Wallace was in a very true sense an evolutionist. He thought of things, and of man's betterment, in an evolutionary way ; he stood by Darwin in fighting the Evolution battle ; and he contributed to our knowledge of the factors in the evolution of living creatures. Yet when he pondered over the origin of the organic from the inorganic, the emergence of consciousness, and the rise of man's most characteristic faculties, he came deliberately to the conclusion that these great steps of progress were due to the influence of an unseen universe

—" a world of spirit, to which the world of matter is altogether subordinate."

He believed in a continuous evolution, but found the scientifically discussable factors quite inadequate to account for the results. Therefore, he said, you must allow me to postulate " different degrees of spiritual influx." Thinking of the origin of living organisms, the emergence of conscious creatures, the rise and progress of man, he was led to believe " that a change in essential nature (due, probably, to causes of a higher order than those of the material universe) took place at the several stages in progress which I have indicated ; a change which may be none the less real because utterly imperceptible at its point of origin, as is the change that takes place in a curve in which a body is moving when the application of some new force causes the curve to be slightly altered " (" Darwinism," 1889, p. 476).

WAS WALLACE RIGHT?

To many minds Wallace's position appears very reasonable. What he said was this : A satisfactory Evolution Theory must be more than *modal*, it must be *causal*. That is to say, it must tell us about the causes that operated in the great process of Becoming. But the scientific evolutionist has very little to tell us about the factors that led to the emergence of *living* organisms, *conscious* organisms, and *human* organisms. These were big steps; can one account for them ? The frank evolutionist admits : There is as yet only a little scientific light on these great uplifts. So little, Wallace replied, that the way seems open to postulate a spiritual influx which intervened to help the process of natural evolution at critical stages. A new kind of cause came into operation to help matter and life over difficult stiles. Yet, he hastily added, never in such a way as to involve a breach of continuity.

WHY WE CANNOT ACCEPT THE IDEA OF RECURRENT SPIRITUAL INFLUXES.

There seem to be several serious difficulties in the way of accepting Wallace's view. First, it is premature to say that Science will not be able to throw much more light on the big steps in evolution—such as the emergence of living organisms, conscious creatures, and human personalities. Second, Wallace's view includes a somewhat unwelcome suggestion, that the original creation (by which we mean the institution of the Order of Nature) was imperfect, and that it was found necessary to intervene with special aid to help the evolving world through difficult crises. Third, it seems to suggest a picture of *two* worlds instead of one, as if the power of God and the Wisdom of God were not, to the religious mind, behind everything all the time, behind the " explicable " as well as the " puzzling." Finally, although Wallace insisted that there was no breach of continuity in his theory of spiritual influxes, just as one might say there was no breach of continuity in accounting for one of our actions in terms of our " body " and for another in terms of our " mind," yet there was a mingling of two sets of ideas that cannot blend. So much, he said, could be described in terms of the factors that science works with, (matter and energy, protoplasm and mind) ; so much demands other and transcendental factors which are beyond science, to wit, " spiritual influxes." But when one is making a journey in a foreign country one must keep to the coinage of that country. We think Wallace's position would have been stronger if he had jettisoned " continuity."

CHARLES KINGSLEY'S PICTURE.

It is very absurd to think that one clears up the problem of origins by pronouncing the word EVOLUTION. One cannot reverse the cosmic cinematograph and see the emergence of the first birds from a stock of extinct Dinosaur reptiles. From the nature of the case, that can never be proved, and yet one is as certain of the fact as one can be about any pre-historic event. But when we say : " Birds evolved from reptiles," we do not delude ourselves by supposing that this tells us how the extraordinary transformation took place. If we cannot yet make clear how a Silver Wyandotte or a White Leghorn has evolved in a short time from the Wild Jungle Fowl of India, how can we expect to be clear in regard to such a " big lift " as the emergence of the first birds ? In all these cases we must simply have patience, and continue probing into the factors that were and are operative in evolutionary changes.

Thus, instead of saying, " This emergence of, say, bird or man is too wonderful for us, too hopelessly beyond science ; we must postulate a spiritual influence," we should rather say : " Here is a brain-stretching problem to be tackled more strenuously." Wallace's position seems to us like trying to subsidise natural processes with grants from a spiritual Treasury. Is there not a stronger philosophy in Charles Kingsley's immortal " Water-Babies " ? When the child at length came to Mother Nature, and, expecting to find her very busy, was surprised at her folded hands, he received to his natural question a wise answer : " You see I make things make themselves." Surely, we have good reason to increase our confidence in what natural processes can do, for every year discloses some new and wonderful possibility.

WHAT LAPLACE TOLD NAPOLEON.

The Nebular Hypothesis thought out by the great French mathematician, Laplace, was a brilliant anticipation of later theories—somewhat subtler and sounder—of the genesis of our solar system. Laplace, in 1796, like the philosopher Kant in 1755, showed the possibility of the establishment of the sun and the planets from a gigantic rotating gaseous mass or nebula ; and there is general agreement to-day as to the nebular origin of our solar system and of others of a somewhat similar nature.

But what concerns us just now is not the Nebular Hypothesis, but Laplace's interview with Napoleon. The story goes that the monarch asked the astronomer what room there was for God in his " celestial mechanics," Laplace replied that he " had no need of that hypothesis," and this answer has been terribly misunderstood. In the first place, we cannot for a moment imagine that there was any lack of seriousness on Laplace's part. No one could be flippant to Napoleon ! In the second place, we may be sure that Laplace was not making a profession of atheism. What Laplace meant was that no one could speak of God and of Gravitation in the same breath. If it is possible to think out a system of " celestial mechanics " which will describe how the solar system had its origin from a nebula in a natural and necessary way, then, for the time being, there must be " celestial mechanics " and nothing more. Laplace meant that the august concept of God is foreign to the astronomer's " universe of discourse," as the philosophers say. Empirical and transcendental concepts must be kept apart. Difficult problems in science cannot be illumined by any religious light.

And yet while the astronomer as astronomer may regard the system of the stars as autonomous or sufficient in itself, requiring no underpinning, no winding-up or regulation like a clock, he may be very religious in the sense that he discerns with the spiritual eye the Power and Wisdom of God, and cannot without this belief think steadily of the significance and purpose of all that his science describes. As the poet wisely said : " The undevout astronomer is mad." So far as we understand these matters, there is no contradiction in accepting as astronomer some form of the Nebular Hypothesis, and yet as a religious man joining with the psalmist in saying : " Lift up your eyes on high, and behold who hath created these things, that bringeth out their host by number ; He calleth them all by name by the greatness of His might ; for that He is strong in power, not one faileth." We admit, indeed, that the last clause may suggest a direct under-pinning in a form from which the modern mind recoils, but does any one suppose that he understands the relation of God to the world ? Our general point is that Laplace's answer expresses the position of the modern evolu-tionist, who declines to mix up transcendental and empirical concepts, and yet may be, like Professor Lloyd Morgan, a convinced theist.

IDEA-TIGHT COMPARTMENTS.

But the critical reader may ask if this is not a return to the old device of idea-tight compart-ments in the mind. Here is the tidy compart-ment of the measurable and registrable, the scientific compartment with its empirical de-scriptions and formulations, where things and their changes are summed up in terms of their lowest common denominators, such as electrons and protons, protoplasm and mind. Here you may ask, " What is this ? How does this work or persist ? Whence came this ? " But you must not ask what is the meaning or purpose of all this Becoming, Being, and Having Been. For that question belongs to another compartment, the religious or theological compartment, where feeling speaks as well as reason, where the light is not cold but warm, where one is awed by the fundamental mysteriousness of Nature, where one cannot repress the characteristic human question : What does all this mean ?

We should indeed be returning to the device of idea-tight compartments if we suggested that our scientific conclusions and our religious convictions had nothing to say to one another. That would be very unphilosophical, for philosophy is the attempt to see things whole, to have a coherent synoptic vision. Our inner life, like our bodily life, must express an endeavour after unity or harmony. Our search after the ideal to which we apply the august word TRUTH is asymptotic ; that is to say, it is like a curve which is always approaching a right line but never reaching it ; and part of the reason for this is that in seeking after truth we have to pursue various methods, of which the scientific method is only one. It is plain, for instance, that our knowledge of our friend, when we know him well, is more than scientific. One of the rights-of-way towards reality is by feeling, which may include religious feeling.

If every result of Science were perfect, as some results are, in the domain of mechanics for instance, then the issue would be clearer. But in the more elusive orders of facts, concerned

with life and mind, there is still a high degree
of inexactness ; and, with the best will in the
world, the scientific investigator may frame a
conclusion that is very far from being perfect.
Reaching conclusions is a very difficult art, and
in spite of himself the investigator may state his
results in a way that is not perfectly justifiable.
And here, we think, the evolutionists have sometimes been at fault. They have allowed their
scientific conclusion to be coloured by their
philosophy. This is most liable to happen when
the scientific investigator says that he has no use
or philosophy.

USE OF METAPHYSICS.

Another unwise thing that scientific investigators occasionally do is to sneer at metaphysics.
But one kind of metaphysics is just a resolute
inquiry into the implications of what we say.
In technical language this is called " a criticism
of categories " ; and it is for lack of meta-
physical training that investigators—especially
in the less exact sciences—have sometimes said
more than they had any right to say. To put it
very shortly, we are all apt to allow our cosmogony, our world outlook, to colour our cosmo-
graphy or our scientific picture.

Even within the exact sciences there is need
for great carefulness in the statement of large

conclusions. Thus all the experts know what they mean by the Conservation of Energy as a laboratory principle, but it is another thing to state it in a form suited for incorporation in Everyman's philosophy. So, *à fortiori*, for the great generalisation summed up in the word EVOLUTION.

Far be it from us to suggest that science can ever dance to theology's piping, that would be hopeless confusion and disloyalty to the truth. What we are suggesting is the need for a philosophical revision of the statement of scientific conclusions in regard to matters where knowledge remains inexact.

WHAT IS TRUTH?

But does not science tell us what is true, and if so, what has philosophy got to do with it? "I ask not proud philosophy to tell me what thou art!" But it would be nearer the mark to say that science tells us what is accurate, which is a contribution towards discovering the truth. One must remember that scientific investigation is like fishing with a net whose meshes have been adjusted to let all but certain orders of fact *slip through*. It is a partial abstract kind of inquiry, and the more rigidly it keeps to its own methods the better science it is. Yet if the physiologist goes out to study the ways of animals in a wood, and comes back telling us that he finds no mind at work in all he saw, it seems reasonable to remember that mind cannot be discovered by physiological methods. Mind is a kind of fish that the physiologist's net cannot possibly catch. Part of the proof of its reality is just that the physiologist's illuminating and invaluable account of the ways of the animals in the wood does not cover all the facts which are discerned by other eyes.

CAN SCIENCE AND RELIGION INFLUENCE ONE ANOTHER?

Our general position, which we have defended elsewhere ("Science and Religion," 1925), is that if science and religion are true to their respective aims there should not be any antithesis between them *as regards essentials*. For science tries to describe or formulate what happens and has happened in terms of the lowest common denominators available at the time, such as electrons, protons, radiations, protoplasm, and mind. Whereas religion seeks to *interpret* Nature and Man's place in it in terms of the Greatest Common Measure, which, for many thinking people, means God.

But if the desirable course is to give over to Science the task that is Science's, and to Religion the task that is Religion's—empirical formulation on the one hand and transcendental interpretation on the other—is there any influence between them ?

The answer is fourfold : (1) That the results of science must be included in the religious outlook—clarifying, widening, and deepening it ; (2) that the facts of religious experience must not be ignored by science ; (3) that religious convictions should not include descriptive statements as to the nature of scientifically observable processes ; and (4) that the way in which scientific conclusions are stated should be carefully scrutinised lest they include elements which are not strictly scientific.

SCIENCE AND RELIGION.

To illustrate concretely each of these points in order :

(1) The religious outlook will be illumined when it includes the scientific concept of organic evolution as the mode of becoming that has been characteristic of Animate Nature.

(2) Science may decline to have anything to do with the religious outlook, but it has no right to make an alternative between a scientific generalisation (such as Evolution) and a religious conviction (such as the reality of a Divine Will). For that is a false antithesis.

(3) If the religiously-minded man states his

conviction that all the different kinds of plants and animals arose as they are in a short space of time, he is trespassing on scientific territory. He is taking up the *rôle* of a describer.

(4) But if Science goes so far wrong as to say that the emergence of man was quite accidental, it is likewise guilty of trespass, and should be prosecuted.

THE GENERAL IDEA OF ORGANIC EVOLUTION.

Samuel Butler compared organic evolution to a fugue. " As in the development of a fugue, where, when the subject and counter-subject have been announced, there must thenceforth be nothing new, and yet all must be new, so throughout organic nature—which is a fugue developed to great length from a very simple subject—everything is linked on to and grows out of that which comes next to it in order— errors and omissions excepted."

The general idea of organic evolution is that the present is the child of the past and the parent of the future. The whole system of Living Nature is seen as a continuous sequence of transformations, in the course of which, apart from conservative types remaining unchanged for millions of years, apart also from eddies, parasitisms, retrogressions and degeneracies, there is, on the whole, a persistent advancement of life, with a continued emergence of the new.

The idea was well expressed in 1794 by Erasmus Darwin. In speaking of Hume he said: " He concluded that the world itself might have been generated rather than created ; that it might have been gradually produced from very small beginnings, increasing by the activity of its inherent principles, rather than by a sudden evolution of the whole by the Almighty fiat." The word " evolution " in this sentence is curious ; it is used where we should use the word " creation " ! But from the sentence as a whole it is plain that Darwin's grandfather was thinking of the analogy between the individual development of an organism from a germ—the chick from the egg—and the age-long production of the world and its inhabitants from " very small beginnings." The butterfly develops from the caterpillar, and that from an egg ; the frog develops from a tadpole, and that from an egg. This is like racial evolution in its continuity and in its gradualness of transformation. But it is unlike racial evolution since the germ is not a very simple beginning, but rather the long result of time, rich in the legacies of past ages.

ORGANIC EVOLUTION DEFINED.

Evolution is a process of Becoming, and the

33   c 2

idea is too big and too wide to be defined. As we shall afterwards see, there are at least three different kinds of evolution—inorganic, organic, and social. We are at present concerned with the rise and progress, the appearing and disappearing, *Werden und Vergehen und Weiter-Werden*, of plants and animals, and of man as organism.

Organic evolution may be defined as a racial movement in a definite direction (or in definite directions), in the course of which new types emerge and survive, either in place of or alongside of those from which they arose, all apparently occurring by continuous processes of change which admit of scientific description or give promise of so doing. When we say continuous we mean that there are no gaps though there may be jerks. When we say " scientific description " we mean that a coherent account is more or less possible in terms of verifiable factors. There is no joukery-pawkery.

MIND IN EVOLUTION.

In working out the history of anything, it is necessary for the scientific investigator to postulate some beginning from which he can start. " Give me material," Kant said, " and I will make a world out of it." So it is quite fair for the biologist to say: " You must allow me to

34

start from the original simplest living creatures. For *them* I cannot account, but if you grant me the first Protists I can outline the story of Organic Evolution."

But in regard to Mind it is necessary to walk warily, for it is not possible to derive mind from something that is not mind. At a certain, or rather uncertain, level in the hierarchy of animals there is a distinct emergence of mind, for we cannot make sense of what the creatures do unless we credit them with some feeling and purposing, some imaging and remembering. Now whatever be our view in regard to the nature of " mind," and its relation, if it be a relation, to " body," we must admit that there is an inner subjective life of feeling, willing, and thinking that cannot be described in terms of chemistry and physics. Yet this inner life *counts for much* and cannot be left out in thinking of the process of evolution. We must assume that there was something corresponding to mind in the first living creatures, just as is true of the first stages in the making of the individual man. And it is one of the great facts of Organic Evolution that as it continued from age to age there was among animals an increasing manifestation of mind. We shall return to this great fact, but it is important to lay down the proposition, which some would call a truism, that

35

whatever Evolution means it is a process involving mind from first to last—if we dare speak of last—and through and through. It was part of the philosophical teaching of Aristotle that there is nothing in the end which was not also in kind in the beginning. Therefore, as we are sure that there is mind in the end, we may also, as evolutionists, say : In the beginning was MIND.

II

GREAT STEPS IN EVOLUTION *

THE Evolution-idea is a master-key that opens many doors. It is a luminous interpretation of the world, throwing the light of the past upon the present. Everything is seen to be an antiquity, with a history behind it—a *natural history*, which enables us to understand in some measure how it has come to be as it is. We cannot say more than " understand in some measure," for while the *fact* of evolution is certain, we are only beginning to discern the *factors* that have been at work.

The evolution-idea is very old, going back to some of the Greek philosophers, but it is only in modern times that it has become an essential part of our mental equipment. It is now an everyday intellectual tool. It was applied to

* This chapter is adapted from " The Outline of Science," edited by Professor J. Arthur Thomson (George Newnes, Ltd.).

the origin of the solar system and to the making of the earth before it was applied to plants and animals; it was extended from these to man himself; it spread to language, to folk-ways, to institutions. Within recent years the evolution-idea has been applied to the chemical elements. Not less important is the extension of the evolution-idea to the world within as well as to the world without. For alongside of the evolution of bodies and brains is the evolution of feelings and emotions, ideas and imagination.

Organic evolution means that the present-day animals and plants and all the subtle inter-relations between them have arisen in a natural knowable way from a preceding state of affairs on the whole somewhat simpler, and that again from forms and inter-relations simpler still, and so on backwards and backwards for millions of years till we lose all clues in the thick mist that hangs over life's beginnings.

THREE KINDS OF EVOLUTION.

Our solar system was once represented by a nebula of some sort, and we may speak of the evolution of the sun and the planets. But since it has been *the same material throughout* that has changed in its distribution and forms, it might be clearer to use some word like genesis. Similarly, our human institutions were once very different from what they are now, and we may speak of the evolution of government or of cities. But Man works with a purpose, with ideas and ideals in some measure controlling his actions and guiding his achievements, so that it is probably clearer to keep the good old word history for all processes of social becoming in which man has been a conscious agent. Now between the genesis of the solar system and the history of civilisation there comes the vast process of organic evolution. The word development should be kept for the becoming of the individual, the chick out of the egg, for instance.

Organic evolution is a continuous natural process of racial change, by successive steps in a definite direction, whereby distinctively new individualities arise, take root, and flourish, sometimes alongside of, and sometimes, sooner or later, in place of, the originative stock. Our domesticated breeds of pigeons and poultry are the results of evolutionary change whose origins are still with us in the Rock Dove and the Jungle Fowl : but in most cases in Wild Nature the ancestral stocks of present-day forms are long since extinct, and in many cases they are unknown. Evolution is a long process of coming and going, appearing and disappearing, a long-drawn-out sublime process like a great piece of music.

lens-shaped nebulæ to be seen to-day in the heavens, rotating about an axis at right angles to the plane of their slight flattening. If these rotating masses are throwing off material from their equatorial planes, then they are behaving like Laplace's hypothetical nebula. But this confirmation of the original form of the Nebular Hypothesis is badly damaged by the conclusion of the experts that these apparently lenticular nebulæ are ordinary spiral nebulæ seen edgewise.

There appear to be great technical difficulties in the way of Laplace's theory that the planets arose by the separation of successive rings which subsequently condensed. The four inner planets should have possessed greater masses than the outer ones—which is not the case. The final sun should be revolving on its axis much more quickly than it actually does (once in twenty-five days). And, again, the equatorial plane of the sun ought, on Laplace's hypothesis, to lie precisely in the mean plane of the planets' orbits, whereas it is inclined seven degrees to such a plane.

SPIRAL NEBULÆ.

The characteristic nebula observable to-day seems to be a whirling mass of gas with a central nucleus and spirally twisted ejected arms emerging symmetrically from opposite ends. Con-

42

densations in the arms of these whirling nebulæ are stars, as Dr. Jeans has suggested, " in the process of birth." When these condensations began to move as detached bodies, vast clusters of stars may have arisen, vast systems like the Milky Way, each system born out of a rotating nebula. " In the spiral nebula," Jeans writes, " we are watching, not the birth of planets, which Laplace attempted to explain by his nebular hypothesis, but the birth of the stars themselves. The process is, in its main outlines, identical with that imagined by Laplace, but on a more stupendous scale."

It might be supposed that the separate stars, set free from a giant nebula, like sparks from a " Catherine-wheel " firework, would proceed to repeat the process on a small scale, thus forming planets. But the experts on cosmogony, like Dr. Jeans, say no. The matter ejected from a giant nebula might readily form more stars than we can see on a clear night, but a small mass will give off only one condensation or none at all. The matter ejected from a small mass might dissipate into space, or it might form a scattered atmosphere around the residual star, or it might in favourable conditions form a companion star. And such a binary or multiple type is common in the heavens. But our solar system could not arise in this way.

The gist of Laplace's theory is that the solar system arose by the rotational break-up of a great nebula. But the difficulties are apparently very great, and they are not removed by starting with a giant spiral nebula like those we see, which may be forming worlds to-day. Thus there has arisen a novel theory of great attractiveness—the tidal hypothesis. The sun and the moon raise trivial tides on the earth to-day, but it is conceivable that they might be immensely greater. So it is thinkable, that a sun, arising perhaps from the condensation of a nebula, might be subject to intense tidal forces due to a passing star. A great jet or gaseous mass might be lifted off from the sun beyond possibility of recall, and might break into vast fragments which became our present planets. They would at first describe orbits under the combined gravitational action of the sun and of the star which caused the cataclysm, and this, as Jeans suggests, may account for the two planes of the solar system ; but, as the passing star receded, they would be left in obedience to the parent sun. In a metaphorical way, then, we may think of the earth and the planets having a bi-parental origin, the one parent the sun, the other a passing star ! If this is the true theory, it shows that things must have been very well thought out. The mere fact that astronomers have evolved to make such a theory seems enough to show that the star was not passing at random.

PLANETESIMALS.

The tidal theory, as stated by Jeans and by Chamberlin and Moulton, postulates a sun as the result of the ingathering of a primal nebula. The close approach of another star is supposed to draw out a secondary nebula of spiral form with great rotational energy. It should be borne in mind that our present-day sun sometimes shoots out solar prominences to heights of nearly 300,000 miles, and at velocities ranging up to 300 miles per second. What may it not have done when provoked by the passing star !

It is supposed that in the arms of the secondary or spiral nebula there appeared knots which condensed to form the cores of the future planets. The earth-moon knot is supposed to have been double. The liquid or solid cores proceeded to gather in the likewise revolving outer material and the still finer dust-like particles which Chamberlin calls planetesimals. In the case of the earth's growth, great importance is attached to the accretion of the finer planetesimal material, and, according to Chamberlin, the earth was built up as a solid body, not fluid or viscous after the condensation of the knots into cores. Only high-brow mathematicians can pronounce on these theories of world-making, but what interests the outsider is that there are such theories, and that the less stable are being eliminated. The general significance of the picture afforded by the theories of the experts is intelligible. They all lead back to a nebula ; and the thought cannot be repressed that if that was the origin of our solar system, and if living creatures by-and-by arose from the dust of the earth, the rain from heaven and the light of the sun, then there must have been in the nebula much more than met the eye, or would have met the eye, had there been any far-off astronomer to see.

THE PLANETS.

According to the revised nebular hypothesis the sun condensed from an immense diffuse nebula, and whirled for a long time by itself, in single blessedness and without any progeny. But after countless ages had passed, the sun came under the influence of another and a greater star, which appeared in the vicinity, if one can speak of vicinity, and all according to law, no doubt. The attractive influence of this passing stranger—somewhat nebulously known, we fear—produced an uncommonly high tide. From opposite sides of the sun, they say, there were drawn out the arms of an enormous spiral nebula.

After the nebulous fiery birth and the receding of the anonymous passing parent, the great arms of the spiral nebula—less, however, than 1 per cent. of the sun's mass—developed knots or nuclei. Four small knots became the cores of the four inner planets. Nearer to the sun than the earth is, arose Venus and Mercury; and further away was Mars. Beyond Mars came the zone of the small planetoids and the planetesimal dust; and outside this were four greater knots, the beginnings of the major planets, namely, Jupiter, Saturn, Uranus, and Neptune.

THE GROWTH OF THE EARTH.

It has been calculated that the newborn earth—the "earth-knot" of Chamberlin's theory —had a diameter of about 5,500 miles. But it grew by drawing planetesimals into itself until it had a diameter of over 8,100 miles at the end of its growing period. Since then it has shrunk, by periodic shrinkages which have meant the buckling up of successive series of mountains, and it has now a diameter of 7,918 miles. But during the shrinking the earth became more varied.

A sort of slow boiling of the internally hot

earth often forced molten matter through the cold outer crust, and there came about a gradual assortment of lighter materials nearer the surface and heavier materials deeper down. The continents are built up from the lighter materials, such as granites, while the beds of the great oceans are made of the heavier materials such as basalts. In limited areas land has often become sea, and sea has often given place to land, but the probability is that the distinction of the areas corresponding to the great continents and oceans goes back to a very early stage.

The lithosphere is the more or less stable crust of the earth, which may have been, to begin with, about fifty miles in thickness. It seems that the young earth had no atmosphere, and that ages passed before water began to accumulate on its surface—before, in other words, there was any hydrosphere. The water came from the earth itself, to begin with, and it was long before there was any rain dissolving out saline matter from the exposed rocks and making the sea salt. The weathering of the high grounds of the ancient crust by air and water furnished the material which formed the sandstones and mudstones and other sedimentary rocks, which are said to amount to a thickness of over fifty miles in all.

It is interesting to inquire how the callous, rough-and-tumble conditions of the outer world in early days were replaced by others that allowed of the germination and growth of that tender plant we call LIFE. There are very tough living creatures, but the average organism is ill-suited for violence. Most living creatures are adapted to mild temperatures and gentle reactions. Hence the fundamental importance of the early atmosphere, heavy with planetesimal dust, in blanketing the earth against intensities of radiance from without, as Chamberlin says, and inequalities of radiance from within. This was the first preparation for life, but it was an atmosphere without free oxygen. Not less important was the appearance of pools and lakelets, of lakes and seas. Perhaps the early waters covered the earth. And water was the second preparation for life—water, that can dissolve a larger variety of substances in greater concentration than any other liquid ; water, that in summer does not readily evaporate altogether from a pond, nor in winter freeze throughout its whole extent ; water, that is such a mobile vehicle and such a subtle cleaver of substances ; water, that forms over 80 per cent. of living matter itself.

Of great significance was the abundance of

carbon, hydrogen, and oxygen (in the form of carbonic acid and water) in the atmosphere of the cooling earth, for these three wonderful elements have a unique *ensemble* of properties —ready to enter into reactions and relations, making great diversity and complexity possible, favouring the formation of the plastic and permeable materials that build up living creatures. We must not pursue the idea, but it is clear that the stones and mortar of the inanimate world are such that they built a friendly home for life.

ORIGIN OF LIVING CREATURES UPON THE EARTH.

During the early chapters of the earth's history, no living creature that we can imagine could possibly have lived there. The temperature was too high ; there was neither atmosphere nor surface water. Therefore it follows that at some uncertain, but inconceivably distant date, living creatures appeared upon the earth. No one knows how, but it is interesting to consider possibilities.

From ancient times it has been a favourite answer that the dust of the earth may have become living in a way which is outside scientific description. This answer forecloses the question, and it is far too soon to do that. Science must often say " Ignoramus " : Science should be slow to say " Ignorabimus."

A second position held by Helmholtz, Lord Kelvin, and others, suggests that minute living creatures have come to the earth from elsewhere, in the cracks of a meteorite or among cosmic dust. It must be remembered that seeds can survive prolonged exposure to very low temperatures; that spores of Bacteria can survive high temperature; that seeds of plants and germs of animals in a state of " latent life " can survive prolonged drought and absence of oxygen. It is possible, according to Berthelot, that as long as there is not molecular disintegration vital activities may be suspended for a time, and may afterwards recommence when appropriate conditions are restored. Therefore, one should be slow to say that a long journey through space is impossible. The obvious limitation of Lord Kelvin's theory is that it only shifts the problem of the origin of organisms (*i.e.*, living creatures) from the earth to elsewhere.

The third answer is that living creatures of a very simple sort may have emerged on the earth's surface from not-living material, *e.g.*, from some semi-fluid carbon compounds activated by ferments. The tenability of this view is suggested by the achievements of the synthetic chemists, who are able artificially to build up substances such as oxalic acid, indigo, salicylic acid, caffeine, and grape-sugar. We do not know, indeed, what in Nature's laboratory would take the place of the clever synthetic chemist, but there seems to be a tendency to complexity. Corpuscles form atoms, atoms form molecules, small molecules large ones.

So far as we know of what goes on to-day, there is no evidence of spontaneous generation ; organisms seem always to arise from pre-existing organisms of the same kind ; where any suggestion of the contrary has been fancied, there have been flaws in the experimenting. But it is one thing to accept the verdict " omne vivum e vivo " as a fact to which experiment has not yet discovered an exception, and another thing to maintain that this must always have been true or must always remain true.

THE FIRST ORGANISMS UPON THE EARTH.

We cannot have more than a speculative picture of the first living creatures upon the earth or, rather, in the waters that covered the earth. A basis for speculation is to be found, however, in the simplest creatures living to-day, such as some of the Bacteria and one-celled animalcules, especially those called Protists, which have not taken any very definite step towards becoming either plants or animals. No one can be sure, but there is much to be said for the theory that the first creatures were microscopic globules of living matter, not unlike the simplest Bacteria of to-day, but able to live on air, water, and dissolved salts. From such a source may have originated a race of one-celled marine organisms which were able to manufacture chlorophyll, or something like chlorophyll, that is to say, the green pigment which makes it possible for plants to utilise the energy of the sunlight in breaking up carbon-dioxide and in building up (photosynthesis) carbon compounds like sugars and starch. These little units were probably encased in a cell-wall of cellulose, but their boxed-in energy expressed itself in the undulatory movement of a lash or flagellum, by means of which they propelled themselves energetically through the water. There are many similar organisms to-day, mostly in water, but some of them—simple one-celled plants—paint the tree-stems and even the paving-stones green in wet weather. According to Professor A. H. Church there was a long chapter in the history of the earth when the sea that covered everything teemed with these green flagellates—the originators of the Vegetable Kingdom.

On another line, however, there probably evolved a series of simple predatory creatures, not able to build up organic matter from air, water, and salts, but devouring their neighbours.

These units were not closed in with cellulose, but remained naked, with their living matter or protoplasm flowing out in changeful processes, such as we see in the Amœbæ in the ditch or in our own white blood corpuscles and other amœboid cells. These were the originators of the animal kingdom. Thus, from very simple Protists the first animals and the first plants may have arisen.

THE CONTRAST BETWEEN PLANTS AND ANIMALS.

However it may have come about, there is no doubt at all that one of the first great steps in Organic Evolution was the forking of the genealogical tree into Plants and Animals— the most important parting of the ways in the whole history of Nature.

Typical plants have chlorophyll; they are able to feed at a low chemical level on air, water, and salts, using the energy of the sunlight in their photosynthesis. They have their cells boxed in by cellulose walls, so that their opportunities for motility are greatly restricted. They manufacture much more nutritive material than they need, and live far below their income. They have no ready way of getting rid of any nitrogenous waste matter that they may form, and this probably helps to keep them sluggish.

Animals, on the other hand, feed at a high chemical level, on the carbohydrates (*e.g.*, starch and sugar), fats, and proteins (*e.g.*, gluten, albumin, casein) which are manufactured by other animals, or, to begin with, by plants. Their cells have not cellulose walls, nor in most cases much wall of any kind, and motility in the majority is unrestricted.

THE BEGINNINGS OF LAND PLANTS.

It is highly probable that for long ages the waters covered the earth, and that all the primeval vegetation consisted of simple Flagellates in the universal Open Sea. But contraction of the earth's crust brought about elevations and depressions of the sea-floor, and in places the solid substratum was brought near enough the surface to allow the floating plants to begin to settle down without getting out of the light. This is how Professor Church pictures the beginning of a fixed vegetation—a very momentous step in evolution. It was perhaps among this early vegetation that animals had their first successes. As the floor of the sea in these shallow areas was raised higher and higher there was a beginning of dry land. The sedentary plants already spoken of were the ancestors of the shore seaweeds, and there is no doubt that when we go down at the lowest tide and wade

55

cautiously out among the jungle of vegetation only exposed on such occasions we are getting a glimpse of very ancient days. *This* is the forest primeval.

FIRST ANIMALS.

Animals below the level of zoophytes and sponges are called Protozoa. The word obviously means " First Animals," but all that we can say is that the very simplest of them may give us some hint of the simplicity of the original first animals. For it is quite certain that the vast majority of the Protozoa to-day are far too complicated to be thought of as primitive. Though most of them are microscopic, each is an animal complete in itself, with the same fundamental bodily attributes as are manifested in ourselves. They differ from animals of higher degree in not being built up of the unit areas or corpuscles called cells. They have no cells, no tissues, no organs, in the ordinary acceptation of these words, but many of them show a great complexity of internal structure, far exceeding that of the ordinary cells that build up the tissues of higher animals. They are complete living creatures which have not gone in for body-making.

THE MAKING OF A BODY.

The great naturalist Louis Agassiz once said

that the biggest gulf in Organic Nature was that between the unicellular and the multicellular animals (Protozoa and Metazoa). But the gulf was bridged very long ago when sponges, stinging animals, and simple worms were evolved, and showed, for the first time, a " body." What would one not give to be able to account for the making of a body, one of the great steps in evolution ! No one knows, but the problem is not altogether obscure.

When an ordinary Protozoon or one-celled animal divides into two or more, which is its way of multiplying, the daughter-units thus formed float apart and live independent lives. But there are a few Protozoa in which the daughter-units are not quite separated off from one another, but remain coherent. Thus Volvox, a beautiful green ball, found in some canals and the like, is a colony of a thousand or even ten thousand cells. It has almost formed a body ! But in this " colony-making " Protozoon, and in others like it, the component cells are all of one kind, whereas in true multicellular animals there are different kinds of cells, showing division of labour. There are some other Protozoa in which the nucleus or kernel divides into many nuclei within the cell. This is seen in the Giant Amœba (Pelomyxa), sometimes found in duck-ponds, or the beautiful Opalina,

which always lives in the hind part of the frog's
food-canal. If a portion of the living matter of
these Protozoa should gather round each of the
nuclei, then *that would be the beginning of a body*.
It would be still nearer the beginning of a body
if division of labour set in, and if there was a
setting apart of egg-cells and sperm-cells distinct from body-cells.

GREAT ACQUISITIONS.

In animals like sea-anemones and jelly-
fishes the general symmetry of the body is
radial; that is to say, there is no right or left,
and the body might be halved along many planes.
It is a kind of symmetry well suited for sedentary or for drifting life. But worms began the
profitable habit of moving with one end of the
body always in front, and from worms to man
the great majority of animals have bilateral
symmetry. They have a right and a left side,
and there is only one cut that halves the body.
This kind of symmetry is suited for a more
strenuous life than radial animals show; it is
suited for pursuing food, for avoiding enemies,
for chasing mates. And *with the establishment
of bilateral symmetry must be associated the
establishment of head-brains*, the beginning of
which is to be found in some simple worm-
types.

58

Among the other great acquisitions gradually evolved we may notice : a well-developed head with sense-organs, the establishment of large internal surfaces such as the digestive and absorptive wall of the food-canal, the origin of quickly contracting striped muscle and of muscular appendages, the formation of blood as a distributing medium throughout the body, from which all the parts take what they need and to which they also contribute.

HORMONES.

Another very important acquisition, almost confined (so far as is known) to back-boned animals, was the evolution of what are called glands of internal secretion, such as the thyroid and the suprarenal. These manufacture subtle chemical substances which are distributed by the blood throughout the body, and have a manifold influence in regulating and harmonising the vital processes. Some of these chemical messengers are called hormones, which stimulate organs and tissues to greater activity ; others are called chalones, which put on a brake. Some regulate growth and others rapidly alter the pressure and composition of the blood. Some of them call into active development certain parts of the body which have been, as it were, waiting for an appropriate trigger-pulling.

Thus, at the proper time, the milk-glands of a mammalian mother are awakened from their dormancy.

EVOLUTION OF MIND.

A human being begins as a microscopic fertilised egg-cell, within which there is condensed the long result of time—Man's inheritance. The long period of nine months before birth, with its intimate partnership between mother and offspring, is passed as it were in sleep, and no one can make any statement in regard to the mind of the unborn child. Even after birth the dawn of mind is as slow as it is wonderful. To begin with, there is in the ovum and early embryo no nervous system at all, and it develops very gradually from simple beginnings. Yet as mentality cannot come in from outside, we seem bound to conclude that the potentiality of it—whatever that means—resides in the individual from the very first. The particular kind of activity known to us as thinking, feeling, and willing is the most intimate part of our experience, known to us directly apart from our senses, and the possibility of that must be implicit in the germ-cell. Now what is true of the individual is true also of the race—there is a gradual evolution of that aspect of the living creature's activity which we call mind. We cannot put our finger on any point and say : " Before this stage there was no mind." Indeed, many facts suggest the conclusion that wherever there is life there is some degree of mind—even in the plants. Or it might be more accurate to put the conclusion in another way, that the activity we call life has always in some degree an inner or mental aspect.

REFLEX ACTIONS.

Among simple multicellular animals, such as sea-anemones, we find the beginnings of reflex actions, and a considerable part of the behaviour of the lower animals is reflex. That is to say, there are laid down in the animal in the course of its development certain prearrangements of nerve-cells and muscle-cells which secure that a fit and proper answer is given to a frequently recurrent stimulus. An earthworm half out of its burrow becomes aware of the light tread of a thrush's foot, and jerks itself back into its hole before anyone can say " reflex action."

The evolutionary method, if we may use the expression, has been to enregister ready-made responses ; and as we ascend the animal kingdom, we find reflex actions becoming complicated and often linked together, so that the occurrence of one pulls the trigger of another, and so on in a chain. The behaviour of the insectivorous plant called Venus' fly-trap when it shuts on an insect is like a reflex action in an animal, but plants have no definite nervous system.

WHAT ARE CALLED TROPISMS.

A somewhat higher level on the inclined plane is illustrated by what are called " tropisms," obligatory movements which the animal makes, adjusting its whole body so that physiological equilibrium results in relation to gravity, pressure, currents, moisture, heat, light, electricity, and surfaces of contact. A moth is flying past a candle ; the eye next the light is more illumined than the other ; a physiological inequilibrium results, affecting nerve-cells and muscle-cells ; the outcome is that the moth automatically adjusts its flight so that both eyes become equally illumined ; in doing this it often flies into the candle.

It may seem bad business that the moth should fly into the candle, but the flame is an utterly artificial item in its environment to which no one can expect it to be adapted. These tropisms play an important *rôle* in animal behaviour.

INSTINCTIVE BEHAVIOUR.

On a higher level is instinctive behaviour,

which reaches such remarkable perfection in ants, bees, and wasps. In its typical expression instinctive behaviour depends on inborn capacities ; it does not require to be learned ; it is independent of practice or experience, though it may be improved by both ; it is shared equally by all members of the species of the same sex (for the female's instincts are often different from the male's) ; it refers to particular conditions of life that are of vital importance, though they may occur only once in a lifetime. The female Yucca Moth emerges from the cocoon when the Yucca flower puts forth its bell-like blossoms. She flies to a flower, collects some pollen from the stamens, kneads it into a pill-like ball, and stows this away under her chin. She flies to an older Yucca flower and lays her eggs in some of the ovules within the seed-box, but before she does so she has to deposit on the stigma the ball of pollen. From this the pollen-tubes grow down and the pollen-nucleus of a tube fertilises the egg-cell in an ovule, so that the possible seeds become real seeds, for it is only a fraction of them that the Yucca Moth has destroyed by using them as cradles for her eggs. Now it is plain that the Yucca Moth has no individual experience of Yucca flowers, yet she secures the continuance of her race by a concatenation of actions which form part of her instinctive repertory.

From a physiological point of view instinctive behaviour is like a chain of compound reflex actions, but in some cases, at least, there is reason to believe that the behaviour is suffused with awareness and backed by endeavour. This is suggested in exceptional cases where the stereotyped routine is departed from to meet exceptional conditions. It should also be noted that just as ants, hive bees, and wasps exhibit in most cases purely instinctive behaviour, but move on occasion on to the main line of trial and error or of experimental initiative, so among birds and mammals the intelligent behaviour is sometimes replaced by instinctive routine. Perhaps there is no instinctive behaviour without a spice of intelligence, and no intelligent behaviour without an instinctive element. The old view that instinctive behaviour was originally intelligent, and that instinct is " lapsed intelligence," is a tempting one, and is suggested by the way in which habitual intelligent actions cease in the individual to require intelligent control, but it rests on the unproved hypothesis that the acquisitions of the individual can be entailed on the race. It is almost certain that instinct is on a line of evolution quite different from intelligence, and that it is nearer to the inborn inspirations of the calculating boy or the musical genius than to the plodding methods of intelligent learning.

The higher reaches of the inclined plane of behaviour show intelligence in the strict sense. They include those kinds of behaviour which cannot be described without the suggestion that the animal makes some sort of perceptual inference, not only profiting by experience but learning by ideas. Such intelligent actions show great individual variability ; they are plastic and adjustable in a manner rarely hinted at in connection with instincts where routine cannot be departed from without the creature being nonplussed ; they are not bound up with particular circumstances as instinctive actions are, but imply an appreciative awareness of relations.

When there is an experimenting with general ideas, when there is *conceptual* as contrasted with *perceptual* inference, we speak of Reason, but there is no evidence of this below the level of man. It is not, indeed, always that we can credit man with rational conduct, but he has the possibility of it ever within his reach.

There is no doubt as to the big fact that in the course of evolution animals have shown an increasing complexity and masterfulness of

65   E 2

behaviour, that they have become at once more controlled and more definitely free agents, and that the inner aspect of the behaviour—experimenting, learning, thinking, feeling, and willing —has come to count for more and more.

THE HAUNTS OF LIFE.

There is another way of looking at the sublime process of evolution. It has implied a mastery of all the possible haunts of life ; it has been a progressive conquest of the environment.

1. It is highly probable that living organisms found their first foothold in the stimulating conditions of the shore of the sea—the shallow and brightly illumined, seaweed-growing shelf fringing the Continents. This littoral zone was a propitious environment, where sea and fresh-water, earth and air, all meet, where there is stimulating change, abundant oxygenation, and a copious supply of nutritive material in what the streams bring down and in the rich seaweed vegetation.

It is not an easy haunt of life, but none the worse for that, and it is tenanted to-day by representatives of practically every class of animals, from infusorians to sea-shore birds and mammals.

THE CRADLE OF THE OPEN SEA.

2. The open-sea or pelagic haunt includes all

the brightly illumined surface waters beyond the shallow water of the shore area.

It is perhaps the easiest of all the haunts of life, for there is no crowding, there is considerable uniformity, and an abundance of food for animals is afforded by the inexhaustible floating " sea-meadows " of microscopic Algæ. These are reincarnated in minute animals like the open-sea crustaceans, which again are utilised by fishes, these in turn making life possible for higher forms like carnivorous turtles and toothed whales. It is quite possible that the open sea was the original cradle of Life, and perhaps Professor Church is right in picturing a long period of pelagic life before there was any sufficiently shallow water to allow the floating plants to anchor.

THE GREAT DEEPS.

3. A third haunt of life is the floor of the Deep Sea, the abyssal area, which occupies more than a half of the surface of the globe. It is a region of extreme cold—an eternal winter ; of utter darkness—an eternal night—relieved only by the fitful gleams of " phosphorescent " animals ; of enormous pressure—$2\frac{1}{2}$ tons on the square inch at a depth of 2,500 fathoms ; of profound calm, unbroken silence, immense monotony. It is probable that the colonising

of the great abysses took place in relatively recent times, for the fauna does not include many very ancient types. It is practically certain that the colonisation was due to littoral animals which followed the food-debris, millennium after millennium, further and further down the long slope from the shore.

THE FRESHWATERS.

4. A fourth haunt of life is that of the freshwaters, including river and lake, pond and pool, swamp and marsh. It may have been colonised by gradual migration up estuaries and rivers, or by more direct passage from the seashore into the brackish swamp. Or it may have been in some cases that landlocked corners of ancient seas became gradually turned into freshwater basins.

CONQUEST OF THE DRY LAND.

5. The terrestrial haunt has been invaded age after age by contingents from the sea or from the freshwaters. We must recognise the worm invasion, which led eventually to the making of the fertile soil, the invasion due to air-breathing Arthropods, which led eventually to the important linkage between flowers and their insect visitors, and the invasion due to air-breathing Amphibians, which led eventually to the higher terrestrial animals and to the development of

intelligence and family affection. Besides these three great invasions, there were minor ones such as that leading to land-snails, for there has been a widespread and persistent tendency among aquatic animals to try to possess the dry land.

Getting on to dry land had a manifold significance.

It implied getting into a medium with a much larger supply of oxygen than there is dissolved in the water. But the oxygen of the air is more difficult to capture, especially when the skin becomes hard or well protected, as it is almost bound to become in animals living on dry ground. Thus this leads to the development of *internal surfaces*, such as those of lungs where the oxygen taken into the body may be absorbed by the blood. In most animals the blood goes to the surface of oxygen-capture ; but in insects and their relatives there is a different idea—of taking the air to the blood or in greater part to the area of oxygen-combustion, the living tissues. A system of branching air-tubes takes air into every hole and corner of the insect's body, and this thorough aeration is doubtless in part the secret of the insect's intense activity. The blood never becomes impure.

The conquest of the dry land also implied a predominance of that kind of locomotion which may be compared to punting, when the body is pushed along by pressing a lever against a hard substratum. And it also followed, that with few exceptions the body of the terrestrial animal tended to be compact, readily lifted off the ground by the limbs or adjusted in some other way so that there might not be too large a surface trailing or sprawling. An animal like a jelly-fish, easily supported in the water, would be impossible on land. Such apparent exceptions as earthworms, centipedes, and snakes are not difficult to explain, for the earthworm is a burrower which eats its way through the soil, the centipede's long body is supported by numerous hard legs, and the snake pushes itself along by means of the large ventral scales, to which the lower ends of very numerous ribs are attached.

NECESSITY AND CURIOSITY.

It is worth dwelling on the risks of terrestrial life, because they enable us better to understand why so many land animals have become bur-rowers and others climbers of trees, why some have returned to the water and others have taken to the air. It may be asked, perhaps, why the land should have been colonised at all when the risks and difficulties are so great. The answer must be that necessity and curiosity are the mother and father of invention. Animals left the water because the pools dried up, or because they were overcrowded, or because of inveterate enemies, but also because of that curiosity and spirit of adventure which, from first to last, has been one of the spurs of progress.

CONQUERING THE AIR.

6. The last great haunt of life is the air, a mastery of which must be placed to the credit of insects, Pterodactyls, birds, and bats. These have been the successes, but it should be noted that there have been many brilliant failures, which have not attained to much more than parachuting. These include the Flying Fishes, which take leaps from the water and are carried for many yards and to considerable heights, holding their enlarged pectoral fins taut or with little more than a slight fluttering. There is a so-called Flying Frog (*Rhacophorus*) that skims from branch to branch, and the much more effective Flying Dragon (*Draco volans*) of the Far East. Among mammals there are Flying Phalangers, Flying Lemurs, and more besides, all attaining to great skill as parachutists, and illustrating the endeavour to master the air which man has realised in a way of his own.

The power of flight brings obvious advantages. A bird feeding on the ground is able to evade the stalking carnivore by suddenly rising into the air ; food and water can be followed rapidly and to great distance ; the eggs or the young can be placed in safe situations ; and birds in their migrations have made a brilliant conquest both of time and space. Many of them know no winter in their years, and the migratory flight of the Pacific Golden Plover from Hawaii to Alaska and back again does not stand alone.

THE EVOLVING SYSTEM OF NATURE.

There is another side of evolution so obvious that it is often overlooked, the tendency to link lives together in vital inter-relations. Thus flowers and their insect visitors are often vitally interlinked in mutual dependence. Many birds feed on berries and distribute the seeds. The tiny freshwater snail is the host of the juvenile stages of the liver-fluke of the sheep. The mosquito is the vehicle of malaria from man to man, and the tsetse fly spreads sleeping sickness. The freshwater mussel cannot continue its race without the unconscious co-operation of the minnow, and the freshwater fish called the bitterling cannot continue its race without the unconscious co-operation of the mussel. There are numerous mutually beneficial partnerships between different kinds of creatures, and other inter-relations where the benefit is one-sided, as

72

in the case of insects that make galls on plants. There are also among kindred animals many forms of colonies, communities, and societies. Nutritive chains bind long series of animals together, the cod feeding on the whelk, the whelk on the worm, the worm on the organic dust of the sea.

THE WEB OF LIFE.

There is a system of successive incarnations, and matter is continually passing from one embodiment to another. These instances must suffice to illustrate the central biological idea of the web of life, the interlinked System of Animate Nature. Linnæus spoke of the Systema Naturæ, meaning the orderly hierarchy of classes, orders, families, genera, and species ; but we owe to Darwin in particular some knowledge of a more dynamic Systema Naturæ, the network of vital inter-relations. This has become more and more complex as evolution has continued, and man's web is most complex of all. It means making Animate Nature more of a unity ; it means an external method of registering steps of progress ; it means an evolving set of sieves by which new variations are sifted, and living creatures are kept from slipping down the steep ladder of evolution.

III

THE FACT OF EVOLUTION

ACCORDING to the evolutionists the different kinds of wild animals and plants are descended from ancestors on the whole somewhat simpler or more generalised, and the process of change has been effected by factors similar to those that are seen in operation in the world to-day. Variations or new departures crop up and these are sifted—this is the *causal* theory held by most naturalists.

NO LOGICAL DEMONSTRATION.

Now the question arises : What is the logical position of this general theory of evolution, without going at present into the question of the factors that have been at work ? It must be conceded at once that the theory cannot be demonstrated like the theory of gravitation ; it cannot be demonstrated by experiment like the doctrine of the Conservation of Energy. It deals in the main with the distant past,

74

and it is logically comparable to the Nebular Hypothesis which gives an account of the genesis of the Sun and its planets. No one can reverse the cosmic film, so as to make visible what happened long ago. Yet it may be pointed out that there are Nebulæ in the sky to-day which are behaving much in the same way as astronomers believe the momentous nebula to have behaved that gave rise long ago to our Solar System. Similarly with Organic Evolution, there are processes going on to-day which resemble those that occurred when Birds emerged from a Reptile stock or Amphibians from Fishes.

WISDOM JUSTIFIED OF HER CHILDREN.

But there are many sound conclusions that cannot be logically demonstrated. Thus it is uncommonly difficult to prove what is called the reality of the material universe around us, and Dr. Johnson's proof—by kicking a stone— was no better or worse than many another with more pretensions. The question is : *How did this world of life arise?* and the only scientific answer in the field is the Evolution answer which states the mode of the Becoming. The world of animal life, with all its exuberant variety, arose in a manner comparable to that by which all our domesticated breeds of pigeons have arisen within recent times from the Rock-dove which still nests on some of the cliffs around Great Britain. The world of plant life, with all its wealth of detailed beauty, arose in a manner comparable to that by which all our garden cabbages, cauliflowers, curly greens, broccoli, brussels sprouts, and so on, are descended from the Wild Kale of the sea-shore. The general idea of Organic Evolution involves an argument from analogy : As in the few cases that Man knows about, his domesti-cated animals and cultivated plants, so has it been through the expanse of Animate Nature.

It is plain, therefore, why we shrink from the familiar title : Evidences of Evolution. For every fact of anatomy and physiology, palæ-ontology and embryology, may be used as an evidence of evolution, if we know enough about it. The argument, if such it may be called, is simply a cumulative illustration of how this master-key opens all manner of locks.

MAN AS TRANSFORMER.

Darwin was greatly interested in man's achievements in domestication and cultivation. There are races of pigeons, say fantails and pouters, which seem to be farther away from one another than are many of the species of birds in Wild Nature. So Darwin's sound argument was : If man can establish in a comparatively short time numerous true-breeding races, what may Nature not have done in a very long time ? What is it exactly that Man does in such cases ? He waits for variations or sports to turn up ; and sometimes he hastens the crop of novelties by crossing. When some new departure emerges that pleases him or suits his needs, he lets it pair with another as like itself as possible. From the progeny he removes those individuals that are furthest from what he desires, and then he brings the best types together in breeding. On the one hand, he weeds ; and on the other hand, he breeds. By consistently pursuing this weeding and breeding, this " artificial selection," as Darwin called it, Man has reached very remarkable results. What a variety of domesticated horses, cattle, sheep, dogs, pigeons, poultry and so on ! What a variety of cultivated wheats, turnips, potatoes, roses, pansies, and so on ! It is worth while going to agricultural and horticultural shows to get vivid instances of evolution still at work. Of course many cases are much more complicated than that of pigeons, for there may be several wild ancestors, as is almost certainly the case with dogs. But that does not affect the cogency of the argument : *If by Man in a short time, what by Nature in a very long time?* One must notice, however, two points : first, that Man does not *create* novelties, he waits, more or less, for their emergence ; second, that the agencies in Wild Nature that operate like Man in eliminating and fostering are, in the main, the struggle for existence and the creature's Will to Live.

THE FOUNTAIN OF CHANGE.

When a naturalist settles down to scrutinise different kinds of creatures that are obviously near relatives, he usually finds a remarkable changefulness. Some organisms are much more changeful than others, and some organs or structures are also more changeful than others, but the frequently observed fact is VARIABILITY. When particular characters are measured, the records often show marked fluctuations. Sometimes everything seems in flux. How difficult it is to find two ruffs that could be confused with one another. How unlike two brothers often are ! People use the expression " as like as two peas," but the one pea may grow into a giant and the other into a dwarf. Professor Lotsy speaks of a series of about 200 specimens of the Common Buzzard in the Leiden Museum, " hardly two of which are alike." We know of some compound corals where the architecture of the polyps or individuals differs on different branches of the same colony. There is a fountain of change within the organism. One has, of course, to distinguish extrinsic differences, which can be traced back to peculiarities in surroundings or in food, from intrinsic or inborn differences that seem to well forth from within. Only to the latter do we apply the term variation or mutation.

LIFE CREEPING UPWARDS.

It is probable that there have been living creatures on the earth and in the waters under the earth for far over a hundred million years. It would not be to their credit if they had not made some progress in that time ! The advancement of life is an eloquent spectacle. One of the philosophers, Lotze, who was also a biologist, has compared it to " an onward advancing melody."

For long ages there were no backboned animals or Vertebrates, only backboneless animals or Invertebrates. But in the Silurian seas there were fishes. Ages passed, and in the time of the Old Red Sandstone, there was an emergence of Amphibians. What steps of progress they seem to have made—the acquisition of fingers and toes, true lungs, posterior nostrils, vocal cords, a movable tongue, a three-chambered heart—and so on. It was an epoch-marking advance, though they remained frog-witted creatures even when they reached their Golden Age in the Carboniferous Period.

Ages passed, and in the Permian there began to appear a motley crowd of Reptiles, evidently a very variable and progressive stock. Some marine, some terrestrial, some aerial, some arboreal, some giants, some dwarfs—there was great diversity among the ancient reptiles. None of them had strong brain-development, but there must have been considerable plasticity. Many of them seem to have become over-specialised, like the Flying Dragons or Pterodactyls, for they became extinct without leading on to anything higher. Some of the ancient Reptiles are continued on in the crocodiles and lizards, and other orders of to-day, but others became lost races, and others gave rise to Birds and Mammals, both of which can be traced back to Dinosaurian ancestors. But the largest fact is the one we want, that there has been throughout the ages a successive emergence of nobler forms of life. The inflorescence of the genealogical tree has grown finer and finer. And to this general fact must be added all the pedigrees preserved in the rocks—of horses and elephants, of crocodiles and camels, of lampshells and ammonites. He who digs may read.

When Darwin was a young man of twenty-six he visited the Galapagos Islands, and one of the things that struck him most was that each of the main islands, parts of a submerged land, had its own species of Giant Tortoise. He tells us that he felt himself " brought near to the very act of creation." No doubt the ten or so different species on the different islands were the results of variations of one original stock which became isolated from one another, for these tortoises cannot swim. They correspond to the Orkney Vole and the St. Kilda Wren, insular varieties established by inbreeding into distinct species.

THE GIANT LIZARDS.

The story of the insulated Giant Tortoises has been often told, but that of the two Giant Lizards is less familiar. Darwin was greatly interested—like Mr. William Beebe after him—in the Giant Marine Lizard, *Amblyrhynchus cristatus*, of the Galapagos. It may be four feet long, and while it has learned to go down into the sea, its cousin Conolophus has remained among the lava-rocks of the interior, and has learned to feed on the fruits of cactuses, with prickles like needles. The point is that we have here almost certainly two divergent scions of a common stock, geologically marooned long ago on Galapagos Land. One has taken to Seaweed and the other to Prickly Pears. How luminous the story is in the light of evolution, how obscure otherwise. And if it be asked why there are not numerous species of Giant Lizard, as of Giant Tortoise, on the various islands of the Galapagos archipelago, the answer must be that Amblyrhynchus can swim from island to island, and is thus unrestricted in its inter-crossing.

WHAT THE ANATOMIST HAS TO SAY.

As regards evolution, the anatomist says, what first impresses me is the way in which the same material of bones and muscles, blood-vessels and nerves, in fore-limbs, for instance, is twisted and moulded into the most diverse forms, such as the wing of a bat and the flipper of a whale, the wing of a bird and the arm of man, the paddle of a turtle and the fore-leg of a horse. They are all different and yet they are all the same. Why should there be this strict adherence to the same fundamental structure unless it be that all are blood-relations?

MUSEUMS OF RELICS.

Man himself is rich in anatomical relics of the past, and the same is true of all the higher animals. The past lingers and lives in the present. This is an evolutionist idea of so much importance and interest that it demands illustration.

The Evolution Theory makes everything an antiquity, for it shows past history lurking in present-day being. Vestigial letters in words, like the " o " in leopard, often tell us something of the history, for the ancients thought that the leopard was a cross between a lion and a panther. Vestigial buttonholes on the cuffs of our jacket take our thoughts back to the time when they were functional. The whalebone whale has two sets of teeth which never cut the gum ; and there are snakes (*e.g.*, Glauconia) with miniature and useless hip-girdles, not to speak of tiny thigh-bones that do not even project through the skin. We ourselves are walking museums of relics, some of them at least on exhibition.

It is a familiar evolution idea, that the living hand of the past is on the present, insisting on making itself felt, but illustrations of this sort of survival are always interesting. It may be illustrated in many ways ; let us begin with Survivals in Customs. We would recommend in this connection Miss Lilian Eichler's book, " The Customs of Mankind " (Heinemann, 12*s.* 6*d.*). It is not a book for the learned ; but ordinary people who have not had time to study the evolution of customs will find it very illuminating. It gives a picturesque account of all sorts of folk-ways in different parts of the world—dealing with etiquette, courtship, marriage, hospitality, table manners, dances, games, and so on. In many curious ways the customs of mankind bear out the central evolution idea, that the present is the child of the past and the parent of the future. But we must beware of false simplicities. Thus it is not the whole story of our hand-clasp to say that in the old days those who wished to " make friends " dropped the weapon and extended the hand unarmed ! Nor is the perennial mother-in-law joke elucidated by the fact that if a Wemba (whoever he may be) sees his mother-in-law approaching, he goes down a side street. On the other hand, on ceremonial occasions not so very long ago people got " etiquettes " telling them where to stand and what to do ; and so we say to-day " That's the ticket."

Among some simple peoples a man must never speak till he is spoken to, and the young men among the Crow Indians show their respect for their sisters by refraining from talking to them. But this is not the explanation of the paucity of conversation at some of our family dinner tables. It may not be erroneous to compare the liberation of the marriage-ripe Loango girl from her little hut to the " coming out " of the modern *débutante*, but one must not press this analogy too far. A good instance of the unbroken continuance of a custom from very early days is seen in throwing rice after the bride and bridegroom ; and, while there are three or four theories as usual, the probability is that the rice expresses symbolically the wish that there may be children—a sentiment which it would not be polite to express in so many words. " Though few realise it, and fewer still would admit it, the gift which the bridegroom gives to his bride bears traces of the old form of marriage by purchase." Yet it is a fallacy to suppose, as some Freudians do, that Adam lives on *unchanged* in our Unconscious.

Is the " bread-and-butter " letter after being a guest at a house the polished vanishing point of the old custom of sending a gift to the kind hostess ? Is a table napkin a survival from the days when it was the custom to carry home substantial samples of the feast ? Why does the street boy spit into his hands before he begins the fight, and why does his father spit on the coin " for luck " ? The custom is older than Christianity. Is our dread of spilling the salt an unconscious reminiscence of the time when salt was very precious and naturally became a symbol of hospitality ? Why do we " touch wood " to avert ill-luck, and why does a barber use a red-and-white pole as a sign ?

Another treasury of instances of " the past in the present " is found in Dr. George C. Williamson's " Curious Survivals " (Herbert Jenkins, 12s. 6d.). Those seem to us most interesting where the original significance has been quite lost, and where there is no question of the persistence being due to their picturesqueness or to our liking for the flavour of the antique.

Thus the egg-rolling at Easter, which still lingers in some parts of the country, is vastly more interesting than the continuance of a curfew-bell. For who now knows why the eggs are rolled down the slope ? We send a guinea as a subscription towards a portrait for our friend because there is a genteel gesture in reverting to the old coin, but who knows why the sportsman who brings down the first bird at a shooting party gets a feather in his cap ?

A morning-coat has two buttons near the small of the back, whose buttonholes, for fixing up the tails away from the mud, have long since vanished. And at the wrist there are two or three buttons and buttonholes usually quite functionless, but occasionally still useable if the wearer, wishes to fold back the end of the sleeve. Perhaps there is some æsthetic reason for the persistence of these relics, and it will be noticed that while the buttonholes are usually quite vestigial, the buttons themselves have not dwindled in size. Here we see the original significance at a glance, but who knows why a " baker's dozen " should be thirteen ? We do not ourselves know why publishers should give the book-trade thirteen copies for the price of twelve ! Mr. Skeat has explained many of these survivals in his book, " The Past at Our Doors " (1913) ; those that linger in costume and in language are very numerous. Many of them are certainly worth knowing, for it is of importance to realise that the past has a lien on the present. Really important, however, is the big fact of which these are but trivial instances, that in spite of all our advances the past still lives in our midst and in ourselves.

SURVIVALS IN ANIMALS' HABITS.

The dog turns round and round on the hearth-rug, recapitulating in its somnolence, when " The Unconscious " often shows face, what the ancestral wolf used to do, untold ages ago, when it tried to make a comfortable couch among the herbage. Some Aberdeen cattle transported to a ranch in California hid their young calves in a thicket when they went to graze in the open—suddenly harking back, after a long lineage of domestication, to a well-known habit of wild cattle, so different in this respect from the more quickly moving wild horses among which the foals totter along after their mothers very soon after birth. Even to this day the cow gives her calf heavy drinks, at long intervals, but the mare gives her foal many short drinks which do not incommode its movements.

THE INERTIA OF THE PAST.

The horse " shying " at a rustle in the hedge-row is almost unwittingly obeying an old-fashioned reaction which saved its ancestors from being bitten by a lunging snake. Every year one reads in the country papers of a dog being shot for sheep-worrying. Joined by some comrades, whom it more or less happened to meet at night, it suddenly loses its loyalty and becomes once more a wolf. In the absence of the master, who has been accepted as the head of the pack, if we understand the dog's mental processes rightly, the guardian of the herds becomes irresponsible ; the conventional re-straints of domestication slip away and the promptings of the old wolfish nature find expression. We wonder that it does not happen oftener. We believe that when a full-grown domestic cat plays with a mouse—a some-what puzzling activity—it is harking back to the habit that many wild mother-carnivores have of playfully showing their offspring how to make a capture. The playfulness of kittens has a different meaning : it is an expression of instinctive promptings that are in line with the future business of life, and it is also an exuberant overflow of the assertive individuality of youth—often with some new departure or originality. Various instances of the living hand of the past are discussed in a fine book of many years ago, Robinson's " Wild Traits in Tame Animals," and everyone can discover others for himself. It is important, however, to see these reawakened wild traits as particular examples of a large fact of life, that the past lives on in the present.

THE GENEALOGICAL TREE.

We see another aspect of the same thing in embryonic development, when the animal climbs up its own genealogical tree, to some extent at least. The tadpole is going to become a frog, but it lingers for a while among the fishes, for instance as regards its heart and circulation. The very lopsided plaice and sole, that rest and swim on their silvery left side, are to begin with quite symmetrical, just like ordinary fishes. At that stage they live near the surface of the sea ; later on they lie on the floor. We must think of this enregistering or engraining of the past as a general characteristic of life, and we may find clear and sometimes uncomfortable illustrations of it in the deepest currents of our own life-stream, often called " the primary Unconscious." For it includes ancestral predispositions and behaviour-tendencies which are not always, to put it mildly, sublimed by the control exercised by our higher selves. The " ape and tiger " that Tennyson speaks of are slow to die !

ECHOES IN OUR BODY.

Everyone knows the aberration of the very great poet who wrote a poem involving the donkey—surely a very engaging subject—but turned realism into ridiculousness by describing how " on the pivot of his skull, he (the donkey) slowly turned his long left ear." Many of us must have met at least one fellow-creature who could emulate the donkey in ear-flapping. This is what we mean by an echo : and we take it very seriously. It is an unusual variation this, the ability to activate the residual muscles of the ear-trumpet or pinna, and of real biological interest. It would be very instructive to know if the vestigial muscles were unusually strong in these ear-flapping individuals, or whether there was an unusual vigour of " nervous energy," if that means anything, that was available for re-awakening the contractility of muscle-fibres that had not moved appreciably for generations.

The facts are that we all have vestigial muscle strands in our external ear-pinna ; that few of us have any power of making them contract ; but that an occasional individual among our fellows can flap his ears like any donkey. It is an astonishing sight to see, a remarkable echo ! We have only seen it twice in a very conspicuous degree, and the effect was weird. Yet one has only to walk along a street where there are many horses, as in Covent Garden, to notice that the trumpet of the horse's ear may be adjusted to localise interesting sounds without there being any movement of the head as a whole. Man's increased mobility of the head as a whole is the obvious explanation of his normal inability to move his ear-trumpet.

ANACHRONISMS IN OUR BODY.

Most of our body is a concatenation of living engines quite as effective as is seen in the mechanical engines of a motor car. To tell the truth, very much more effective, though with corresponding possibilities of going wrong. But alongside of this integrated efficiency there linger numerous anachronisms or relics. The same unprofitably persistent out-of-date-ness is occasionally seen in man's devices. It means, for our body, that the past lives on in the present, and that we inherit a few useless relics along with our great wealth. It cannot be said, however, that the influence of the past is even-handed, for there is far more on the " plus " side than on the " minus."

THE THIRD EYELID.

A good example of a vestige is the minute third eyelid or nictitating membrane which we see as a little tag in the inner corner of our eye. It is larger in some races than in others, but it is quite useless. It is a dwindled relic of the large and useful third eyelid that we may see in a rabbit or a dog. It is present in most reptiles and mammals, and in all birds ; and its use is to clean the front of the eye. We often see the bird flick it across. It is pulled down by two special muscles, and then it jerks back of itself, like the blind in a railway carriage. It is absent in whales because the eye is continually washed with water. It is a vestige in man and monkeys because of the greatly increased mobility of the upper eyelid. The word " because " in both these sentences is somewhat elliptical ; we mean that structures not needed tend to disappear.

THE PAST LIVING AND ACTING IN THE PRESENT.

The anatomist has often found pleasure in explaining how the structure of the body, as in the ear-trumpet and the third eyelid, illustrates the lien that the past has on the present.

But while survivals in structure are thus well-known, the idea of survivals in function is less familiar. It has been illustrated in the course of a very fine essay by Professor Marcus S. Pembrey, included in a collective work entitled "Evolution in the Light of Modern Knowledge" (Blackie and Son, London, 1925).

It is evident that in the active and normal life of the body we cannot expect to find the *exact* counterparts of vestigial structures or anatomical relics. For a vestigial structure is practically inactive, and we are now inquiring into activities. Yet there are echoes of the past even in the actively living. Thus the kinds and the proportions of salts in our blood bear a close resemblance to the salts in the sea, especially, they say, to the salts in the ancient Cambrian Sea, when the blood was first evolved and set apart as an internal medium of the animal body.

Before there were warm-blooded animals (birds and mammals) which are able to keep up an almost constant body temperature, day and night, summer and winter, there were cold-blooded animals, like fishes and reptiles, whose body temperature approximates to that of their surroundings. But the newborn babe has not yet acquired the power of maintaining a constant level of body-warmth. The past is echoing, and an incubator is sometimes necessary to keep it from echoing too loudly !

THE INFANT'S GRASP.

Many of us are familiar with the strength of an infant's grip. Even with the big toe there is a notable power of grasping things, and children born without arms and hands will learn to use their feet for purposes of manipulation. As to the hands, Professor Pembrey tells us that " infants on the first day of their separate existence can hang by their hands from a horizontal bar and support their own weight, it may be for as long as two minutes, a longer time than most adults would endure." This is another echo, taking our thoughts back to the time when the ancestors of tentative men served their arboreal apprenticeship. For it can hardly be doubted that the offspring of long ago were carried about by their parents and held firmly on to the long hair.

Another of Professor Pembrey's examples takes us into a different field. Children have often a great liking for raw fruit and raw vegetables (turnips for choice), and this is not to be regarded as a meaningless vagary. It is an echo of primitive diet, and these raw stuffs are very rich in constituents that favour growth. " The petty pilfering of orchards by children should be regarded as a sign, not of original sin, but of an instinctive desire for vitamines."

STRAWS THAT SHOW HOW THE WIND HAS BLOWN.

We see then in many different ways that it is characteristic of the living creature to be able to enregister its experience within itself. Dexterities are acquired, associations are established, habits are formed, and in higher grades of life mental impressions can be retained and revived in true memory. In a way more difficult to understand there is an enregistration of structural gains and profitable new departures ; the racial capital grows at compound interest. Often, along with the racial treasure, there is an hereditary persistence of what has ceased to be very relevant, and when these firmly gripping old-fashioned characters have ceased to be of any use and have dwindled greatly, we call them vestigial structures. We have instanced the little third eyelid in the inner corner of our eye.

The past has a lien on the present, and the animal climbs up its own genealogical tree. When mind comes to count for much, the past lingers in the Unconscious, subject, however, to change, like every other part of the organism. Finally, the past may live on, outside individuals altogether, in the traditional customs of society ; and here, as we have seen, there are often

anachronisms that have lost all meaning. **But**
they remain as straws which show how the
evolutionary wind has blown.

GENEALOGICAL TREES.

Over some of the other so-called " evidences
of evolution " we must pass more quickly.
There are far more than a quarter of a million
different kinds of animals, the great majority of
which are insects. Then there are the myriads
of flowering and flowerless plants. We are in
presence of inexhaustible resources, and we
might think of a restless artist strewing his studio
floor with sketches. But when we look into
these species, or kinds—each itself and no other,
though often showing many variations—we are
soon impressed by the fact that we can arrange
them in orderly series, and we can *sometimes*
make quite plausible genealogical trees. It is
true that our colleague, who works at the same
group of animals, often cuts down the genealogical tree we have cultivated, and seems to find
great pleasure in so doing. But this is welcome
criticism, and it cannot go on indefinitely. Stouter
genealogical trees are being grown.

CONNECTING LINKS.

There is a widespread idea that connecting
links between different types are always missing,
but this is far from being true. Take the oldest

known bird, for instance, Archæopteryx, a fossil from the Jurassic period. It is a good illustration of a connecting link between Birds and Reptiles. For while it had feathers and other undeniable bird-characters, it had teeth in both jaws, a long lizard-like tail, a half-made wing with claws on three digits, and such a little detail as " abdominal ribs." No doubt this is a striking case, but there are many others almost as good.

TRANSFUSION OF BLOOD.

It has been shown that there is harmonious mingling of the blood of horse and ass, hare and rabbit, orang and gibbon, chimpanzee and man. The harmonious mingling is a tell-tale evidence of literal blood-relationship, though that between chimpanzee and man is very remote. But if the blood of a horse is transfused into that of a monkey, or a rabbit's into a dog's, implying a mixture of quite different types, there is great disturbance, and, it may be, destruction of red blood corpuscles. This line of experiment has been followed into subtle detail, and it is actually possible to get a measure of the degree of relationship. Wherever we choose to look, we find interesting facts which admit of evolutionist interpretation, but are puzzling on any other view. So we get the impression of multitudinous facts all pointing in the same direction, all pointing to the idea that it is by evolution that living creatures have come to be as they are, not only in themselves, but in their fascinating inter-relations in the web of life with its pattern that changes from age to age.

But it is not enough to have what is called a *modal* theory of the way things have come to be ; it is necessary to have a *causal* theory ; and that is what biologists are busy with—a theory of the factors in Organic Evolution.

But behind this, in the minds of all who think deeply, there rises the insistent question : What is the meaning, the significance, the purpose, of all this age-long groaning and travailing ? But Science does not ask, far less try to answer, this question. The only answers are religious or philosophical.

IV

HOW EVOLUTION WORKS

SIFTING AND SINGLING.

In human society new departures are common, but few survive the tests of practicability. Somewhat in the same way, new departures or variations are of frequent occurrence in Animate Nature, but only a few survive. The struggle for existence involves a continual sifting of the novelties that crop up, and this seems to be the main method of Organic Evolution. Of great importance also is the question whether a change that makes its appearance in the individual lifetime, as the direct result of some peculiarity in surroundings, food, or habits, can be in any degree entailed on the next generation. For if it is not entailable, in some measure at least, it cannot be of direct *racial* importance. Thus Heredity is one of the conditions of evolution. It is another sieve. We may say, then, that the process of organic evolution is a long-drawn-out commentary on the text : " Test all things and hold fast that which is good."

THE ORIGIN OF THE NEW.

This is the most difficult problem in Biology : How do novelties arise ? In the seventeenth century there appeared in an apothecary's garden in Heidelberg a Greater Celandine with much cut-up leaves. It was named the variety *laciniatum* of the species *Chelidonium majus*, and its particular interest is that it has bred true ever since. It was a novelty that came to stay. But the question is : How did it arise ?

When Charles I. was king in England there was a Frenchman called Jean Nougaret, who suffered from a defect called night-blindness. It is not so much a disease as a deficiency. It means inability to see in faint light ; it seems to be due to imply an inadequate equipment of " visual purple " in the retina. Now the record of Jean Nougaret's descendants has been carefully kept, and it is known that in every generation there has been a representation of " night-blind " individuals. If a normal descendant married a normal unrelated person, the spell was broken ; there were no night-blind children. But if a night-blind descendant married a normal unrelated person, the night-blind peculiarity was continued in a certain number of the off-spring. The peculiarity of night-blindness illustrates what is called Mendelian inheritance. But there is a previous question : How did the night-blindness begin ?

Why are the members of a family so often very different from one another ? How can one account for the occasional occurrence of tailless kittens, hornless calves, white blackbirds, spine-less cactuses, seedless oranges, lop-eared and long-haired rabbits, and so on through a lengthy list ? How does the new arise ? The question becomes more urgent when we come to know a sporting plant like Lamarck's Evening Prim-rose (*Œnothera lamarckiana*), which throws off what look like new species in rapid succession—novelties which, in many cases, breed true. A sporting animal which has been much studied of recent years is the American Fruit Fly (*Drosophila ampelophila*), which has given origin to many novelties in a short time. But these are merely signal instances of the variability that is common among living creatures.

SHUFFLING THE HEREDITARY CARDS.

In a way that is beyond our power of pictur-ing, there is in an egg-cell or a sperm-cell, a condensed representation of the hereditary characters. The germ-cell is like a pack of cards which have to be played in the course of its development. It is not to be supposed that what Harvey called the "minting and coining" of the chick out of the egg is like the unpacking of a tightly-packed portmanteau. The germ-cell has "initiatives" that make up the natural inheritance of the species, but these "initiatives" may give rise to other initiatives in the course of development. As a matter of fact we know in some cases, especially in the more primitive animals, like fishes among Vertebrates, that the development of certain characters depends on the movements and surroundings of the young creature. In other words, the hereditary "initiatives" (technically called "factors" or "genes") are not like cheques that have to be cashed, but rather like living seeds which have to be sown. The developing body, which some of them set a-going, is the seed-plot of others. Many biologists think that the hereditary "factors" or "genes" are like little bags of ferments! Now, we know that in the ripening of the germ-cells and in the fertilisation of the egg-cell by the sperm-cell (the usual beginning of an individual life), there are ample opportunities for shuffling the "hereditary cards," by which we mean the "initiatives." It is practically certain that the permutations and combinations that arise in this way find expression in the course of development as new departures or variations.

THE LIVING KALEIDOSCOPE.

The lively and beautiful ruffs which used to nest in Britain show extraordinary variability among the males. It is often said that no two male ruffs are alike, though the females, or reeves, are very uniform. This is the problem—the fountain of change ! Every one knows that a great variety of patterns can be obtained by turning the fragments of coloured glass in a kaleidoscope. Perhaps the germ-cell is a living kaleidoscope. Sometimes it may be influenced by peculiarities in the food, surroundings, and habits of the parent. Sometimes, perhaps, it is stimulated by some deeply-saturating external influence, such as a change of climate. Sometimes, perhaps, the kaleidoscope turns itself, so to speak, affecting spontaneous re-arrangement and re-organisation of its materials. For the germ-cell is living ; it is an implicit organism ; a creature telescoped down, so to speak, into a one-cell phase of being. We have already spoken of the shuffling of the hereditary cards in the maturation and fertilisation of the germ-cells, but perhaps we should think of the origin of the new as, sometimes at least, more *vital*. It looks as if the germ-cells made experiments in self-expression ; perhaps there is a mental aspect to some kinds of variability.

THE ETERNAL PROTEUS.

The Greeks expressed the idea of variability in the myth of Proteus, who changed very readily from form to form, and the same capacity for elusiveness was characteristic of some of the genies of the Arabian Nights. Perhaps " genes " are like " genies " ; perhaps the organism is like Proteus.

VARIATIONS AND MUTATIONS.

A child is often very like one of its parents in some feature, yet a little " more so." Quantitative variations seem to be very common—a little more of this and a little less of that, and these were the variations which Darwin regarded as forming the raw materials of evolution. There are some fossil series which show the transition from one form to another, and, if the preservation of the series can be regarded as anything like complete, what is suggested is *progress by gradual increments*, or, it may be, reductions. There is often a suggestion of definite variation in one particular direction. The different stages are like the successive chapters in individual development.

But there is another kind of change that is more abrupt or brusque ; and this is called a *mutation*. It is a more crisply-cut novelty, such as " crinkly " hair, " angora " hair, a musical genius, a calculating boy, a weeping willow, a copper beech, a long-tailed cock, a white elephant. Sir Francis Galton compared the small variations to the minor oscillations of a shaken polygon, and a mutation to its tumbling on to a new face altogether. One of the interesting features of mutations is that they are very heritable. When they come, they come to stay, if similar possessors are paired together. If genius married genius there would probably be more geniuses. In many cases, it must be noted, a mutation has, so to speak, a *minus* sign—no pigment, no tail, no horns, and so on. But there *are* also *positive* mutations.

NATURE'S SIFTING.

The essence of Darwin's theory of evolution is the sifting of new departures, the winnowing of tentatives. Take the diagrammatic case of the Praying Mantises with which an Italian naturalist, Cesnola, experimented. This quaint insect, *Mantis religiosa*, preying rather than praying, occurs in two varieties, green and brown, suited in their coloration for different habitats. Cesnola tethered brown Mantises with silk thread on withered herbage, and they escaped their enemies. Similarly with green Mantises on green plants. But when he tethered brown individuals on a green background, they were soon picked off by birds ; and similarly, with green individuals on a brown background. Should Italy become a very arid country, the green variety of Mantis would be eliminated, the brown variety would probably survive. This is an instance of what is meant by Natural Selection, a term which we should always translate into Nature's Sifting.

ARTIFICIAL SELECTION.

Darwin's use of the term *Natural* Selection was in contrast to man's *Artificial* selection. When a domesticator or a cultivator sees a new departure that pleases him, he puts it aside and pairs it with another as like itself as possible. In cases like the self-fertilising pea it is of course unnecessary to have more than one parent. Scrutinising the offspring (" the first filial generation "), the breeder or cultivator proceeds to get rid of those that do not show the characters he desires. Thus there is a twofold process, (*a*) of bringing similar " desirables " together, and (*b*) of eliminating the " undesirables."

But what in Wild Nature takes the place of the selective breeder or cultivator ? Part of the answer was the special contribution that Darwin and Wallace made to the Theory of

Evolution. The answer was Natural Selection, especially all the winnowing that occurs in the course of the struggle for existence.

THE STRUGGLE FOR EXISTENCE.

Darwin used this phrase " in a large and metaphorical sense including dependence of one being on another, and including (which is more important) not only the life of the individual, but success in leaving progeny " (" Origin of Species," p. 50). To understand Darwinism we must share Darwin's broad view; by the struggle for existence he meant much more than internecine competition around the platter of subsistence.

Living creatures tend to become numerous ; many of them have a strong will to live ; many are unsatisfied and insurgent ; they resent uncomfortable changes in their surroundings ; and thus comes about the struggle for existence —the clash between organisms and their environing difficulties or limitations. It may be competition to the death, but it may take the form of mutual aid and sociality. It may be for foothold or for food, but also for such a luxury as a fifth wife. It may be for individualistic possession or for the proud pleasure of having a vigorous and affectionate family. It may certainly be a matter of tooth and claw, but it may also rise to a gentle endeavour after well-being. The sifting may imply a sudden " off with his head," but it works out the same result if the relatively less fit organisms have a shorter, harder life and a smaller, less successful family. The important point is, that while the answer-back that saves the situation in the struggle for existence may be making more armour and sharper weapons, it may also be building a warmer nest and having an abundant flow of milk.

DIFFERENT KINDS OF SIFTING.

To make a perfect lawn we have to get rid of all but grass. We may achieve this by digging up all the weeds, and this corresponds to *lethal* selection in Nature. But we might also use a " differential fertiliser," some kind of manure or tonic that stimulates the growth and multiplication of the grass, but not of the weeds. The vigorous grass is soon " too many " for the weeds. This corresponds to what is called in Nature *reproductive* selection, for many creatures succeed in great part not because they are strong or clever, but because they are *many*. Both methods may work together.

Darwin attached great importance, also, to Sexual Selection, that is to say, to those forms of mating in which the female gives the preference to the male that interests and excites her most, in many cases through his display of agility and vigour, or through his song and other æsthetic qualities. It was Darwin's shrewd belief that when the female, let us say bird, held the sieve in this way, it would gradually work towards the evolution of such masculine characters as decorative plumage and musical talent. The difficulty often felt, that these qualities should be handed on to female off-spring as well as to the males, is met by the subsidiary theory that they are indeed handed on to the females, but cannot find expression because the essential feminine constitution inhibits their development.

ISOLATION.

On the island of St. Kilda there is a particular species of wren that is not found anywhere else, and there are many similar cases. The Red Grouse is the particular property of Britain and almost sacred. We have already referred to the ten or so Giant Tortoises on ten or so islands of the Galapagos Archipelago. It is almost certain that these ten or so giants are all descended from one species, that was geologically marooned long ago in Galapagos Land.

Quite apart from islands, there are other ways

of bringing similar forms together, and this means in-breeding. All these ways of shortening the pairing leash correspond to what the human breeder does in bringing similar forms together. Thus the technical term *isolation* is used to sum up all the different ways in which the range of inter-crossing is narrowed, with the result that in-breeding occurs. It may be that similar variants are ripe at the same time ; it may be that some topographical change like a flow of lava or a glacial moraine divides a species into two, which then proceed to diverge ; it may be that similar forms attract one another ; and so on. In-breeding tends to fix and stabilise a stock ; out-breeding tends to promote variability. In many cases, no doubt, they have alternated in the course of evolution.

Looking backwards, then, we may distinguish (*a*) the originative factors in organic evolution, which give rise to variations and mutations, and (*b*) the sifting and singling factors—selection and isolation—which operate on the raw materials that are forthcoming. But our knowledge of the factors of evolution is still very young.

GROWING AND MULTIPLYING.

Stars are formed, crystals grow, but living creatures grow and *multiply*. It is one of the differential characters of organisms that they give rise to other organisms like themselves. This must depend fundamentally on the living creature's power of accumulating matter and energy, and of asking for more, the more they get. The whole economy of Nature is based on the green plant's capacity for accumulating capital. Having the secret of photo-synthesis, which the physical chemist is beginning to wrest from them, the green plants use the energy of the orange-red rays of the sunlight to build up out of carbon dioxide and soil-water an abundance of carbohydrates, fats, and proteins—far more than they need, even when they grow as a tree in bulk. Thus plants feed animals, and one animal feeds another, and incarnation succeeds incarnation, and capitalisation continues. What storage of potential chemical energy there is in a field of oats ; its transformation into kinetic energy is familiar when the horse has had its feed or the workman his porridge. But our point at present is that beyond the capture of the food required for daily needs, the living creature stores, and the storage is expressed in growth ; and reproduction, at its simplest, is discontinuous growth.

GENERATION AFTER GENERATION.

A strawberry plant accumulates much more

potential energy than it needs; it must dispose of this in some way. It grows larger, but there are subtle reasons regulating the best size of leaf and so on, so it becomes profitable to send out a runner which starts a second plant at some distance from the old one. If the runner should decay or be broken, there are two strawberry-plants instead of one. There are two generations, and we do not in this case puzzle over the resemblance between offspring and parent because we know that the offspring arose from an extension of the parental body. Similar material, becoming discontinuous, starts a new individual, " a chip of the old block " as they say. And what is true of the strawberry plant is true of all ordinary plants and animals, except that many kinds of improvements have arisen which have made the survival and success of the new generation a certainty in conditions less easy than those which the strawberry plant has to face.

BUDS AND EGGS.

Hanging to the minute green shoots of the Duckweed (Lemna), the second smallest flowering plant in Britain, there lives the freshwater polyp or Hydra discovered by the Abbé Trembley in the eighteenth century. It is a small tubular animal, about half an inch long and as

thick as a needle. It hangs head downwards
with its mouth surrounded by mobile tentacles
by means of which it can capture and paralyse
minute animals that pass by. When it is pros-
pering, the Hydra accumulates capital, and it
deals with its surplus material by forming
daughter buds, literal reproductions of itself.
If food is very abundant, the daughter buds may
bud off granddaughter buds ; but if a check
to nutrition comes, the offspring all go separate
and the pond is peopled with polyps. Thus,
as in the case of the strawberry plant, we see
that reproduction may be very little more than
discontinuous growth.

What particularly pleased the Abbé Trembley and led him to call his polyp Hydra, after
the wound-defying monster with which Hercules
contended, was his discovery that small parts
readily grew into wholes. If he cut the Hydra
into five parts—we cannot speak of pain at this
low level of brainless life—then he had five
polyps instead of one. Among simple living
creatures a part is often as good as a whole.
It is plain, then, that multiplication might be
effected by separating off small parts instead of
giving off large outgrowths like runners or buds.
This leads us to recognise the essential simplicity of sexual reproduction, where what are
liberated from the parent or parents are not big

pieces but microscopic units—the egg-cells or ova and the sperm-cells or spermatozoa. And if we put the polyps in a watch-glass and look at them under the microscope, we are sure to see some of them with minute protuberances—(a) the ovary (usually in the singular) producing ova, of which, in most cases, only one succeeds ; and (b) the testes (usually in the plural) producing very numerous, extremely minute, sperm-cells, by one of which the ovum is fertilised. The Hydra, it must be noticed, is sometimes a male animal, producing only sperms, and sometimes a female animal, producing only ova or one ovum ; but sometimes the same individual is both male and female at once, as is the case in earthworms, leeches, land-snails, and many other hermaphrodite animals. What is much more unusual is the fact that a Hydra can fertilise its own egg ; for although an earthworm, for instance, is both male and female at once, its eggs are fertilised by sperms from another earthworm. In other words, even when the sexes are combined in one animal, cross-fertilisation is the rule.

ADVANTAGES OF THE GERM-CELL METHOD OF MULTIPLYING.

But if the Hydra multiplies readily by budding and separating off the buds, and if the pond is peopled in this way, the question arises why sexual reproduction by means of eggs and sperms should ever have arisen ? Part of the answer is that the germ-cell method is likely to be more economical to the parent ; that it admits of large numbers of potential lives being started at once, which is of great importance when the chances of death are many ; that it greatly reduces the risk of defects of the individual parent being continued in the offspring ; and that, when there are two parents, the combining of sperm-cell with egg-cell at the beginning of each new life makes it more likely that novelties will crop up, and variability is a vital quality worth running some risks for. Looking far ahead, as it were, the evolutionist can see that the replacement or supplementing of asexual multiplication by sexual multiplication led on to the divergence of males and females—sperm-producers and egg-producers—with different constitutions. And this led on, in the course of time, to the emergence of the gentler emotions and to such flowers of life as the love of mates and a mother's tender care.

WHY LIKE BEGETS LIKE.

We understand why a strawberry plant at the end of a runner should be like the parent plant ; but why should a chick that comes out of an egg develop into a living image of its mother ? The answer is the same in the two cases—there is a persistence of a particular kind of organisation and activity. When a fertilised egg-cell, with certain qualities ($abc \ldots xyz$), is developing into an embryo, it shows a remarkable division of labour among the thousands of cells into which it divides. For development always comes about by the dividing and re-dividing of the egg-cell. Some of the embryo cells become nervous, emphasising, let us say, the quality of irritability (a); others become muscular, emphasising, let us say, the quality of contractility (b); others become glandular, emphasising the secretory quality (c); and so forth. What is called differentiation sets in— the structural side of division of labour. But while this is going on in the building-up of the body, there are certain cells which remain apart and do not share in body-making. They retain the full equipment of the hereditary qualities which we have called $abc \ldots xyz$. These cells, then, that keep up " the continuity of the germ-plasm " form the future reproductive cells— whether egg-cells or sperm-cells. When, in the course of time, they are liberated, with the original qualities $abc \ldots xyz$ unchanged, they will, in favourable conditions, develop into the same kind of creature as the parent. Given the same kind of material to start with, and the same conditions in which to develop, *like tends to beget like*. But, as we have seen, the hereditary tendency to resemblance is not so rigid that it forbids the tendency to vary.

HEREDITY.

Of the three Fates that determine the course of our life—heredity, function, and environment—the greatest is heredity. For the original endowment is more fundamental and far-reaching than the direct influence of habits and surroundings, important as these are. We mean by heredity the flesh-and-blood continuity that binds generation to generation. It is not a Force or a Principle, but an organic linkage sustained by the germ-cells.

THE VEHICLES OF INHERITANCE.

The inheritance includes all that the living creature is or has to start with, and the vehicles of this inheritance are the germ-cells—namely, in all ordinary cases, the egg-cell and the fertilising sperm-cell. Ingenious experiments have proved that a great part of the inheritance— some would say all of it—is carried in the nuclear rods (or chromosomes) of these germ-cells. In a few cases it seems possible to say that such and such a hereditary item (called, as we have mentioned, " factor " or " gene ") is carried by a particular chromosome and in a particular region of that chromosome. Influences or materials seems to pass from the nucleus of the egg-cell into the surrounding living matter, and bring about the establishment of " organ-forming substances "—portions of the living matter that will develop into particular structures in the embryo. And as the fertilised egg-cell divides and re-divides, and begins to form embryonic structures like skin, nervous system, food-canal, and so on, there is an emission of more materials, by which one part influences the development of another. Thus a little piece of a tadpole's developing eye may be grafted underneath the skin of the side of the body, and in that inappropriate place it will provoke the skin to make a lens !

DO THE PARENTS COUNT EQUALLY?

The two parents contribute an equal number of chromosomes to the fertilised egg-cell, but the contributions are not identical in the hereditary factors they carry, and the offspring may take after the father in one character and after the mother in another. But the female parent must always count for more than the male parent, for the egg-cell is equipped with building materials that the sperm-cell lacks. If there is a vital partnership before birth between the mother and the offspring, then the mother will in another way count for more than the father.

Everything points to the conclusion that the whole of the inheritance in the strict sense is contained in the fertilised egg-cell. The potential living creature and its inheritance are, to begin with, one and the same. But the degree to which the initiatives of the inheritance find expression is greatly influenced by the food, the surroundings, and the activities of the developing organism. Hereditary " Nature " and environing " Nurture " work into one another's hands.

MENDELISM.

Johann Mendel was born in Austrian Silesia in 1822, in the same year as Francis Galton, another great student of heredity. His father was a small peasant proprietor, much interested in fruit-culture. At the age of twenty-one he was admitted as a monk, with the " religious " name of Gregor, to the monastery of Brünn, in Bohemia. In 1851 he went for two years to the University of Vienna, where he studied physics and natural science. Returning to his cloister, he acted as teacher of science in the Realschule of Brünn, and occupied his spare time in making experiments with peas and other plants in the garden of the monastery.

In so doing he discovered a new idea in regard to heredity, and reached the very important conclusion often briefly referred to as " Mendel's Law." This was published in 1866 in the *Proceedings of the Natural History Society of Brünn*, but it was practically buried for the rest of the century. Those who knew of it failed to realise its importance, and it was not till 1900 that there was a re-discovery and confirmation of Mendel's work by De Vries in Holland, Correns in Germany, and Tschermak in Austria—and a new era began.

Mendel was undoubtedly a man of great ability in many directions—a successful teacher, a good business man, a keen chess-player, and a determined investigator. He experimented in many directions, but some of his papers have been lost. It is especially to be regretted that there is no record of Mendel's observations on heredity in bees. He had about fifty hives in the garden of the cloister, and he experimented on the crossing of queens of different races—a very promising line of investigation. It is possible that Mendel destroyed his notes amid the disappointments of his later years.

THE GIST OF MENDELISM.

There are three foundation-ideas in Mendelism. The first is the idea of unit-characters, that the inheritance, in part at least, is made up of numerous more or less clear-cut, crisply defined, non-blending characters, which are continued in some of the descendants, as intact items, without merging and without dividing. If a man has his fingers all thumbs, with two joints instead of three, this unit-character of " brachydactylism " will be continued in a certain proportion of his descendants. The long persistence of the Hapsburg lip in the royal houses of Austria and Spain is well known. Sometimes the character is quite trivial, like a white lock of hair; sometimes it is very important, like a tendency to bleeding in males. As we have seen, the unit-characters have their representatives in the nuclear rods or chromosomes in the egg-cell and sperm-cell, and these representatives are called " factors " or " genes " or " determinants."

TAKING AFTER ONE SIDE OF THE HOUSE.

The second big idea in Mendelism is dominance. If a Japanese waltzing mouse, with its constitutional peculiarity of dancing round and round on the slightest provocation, is crossed with a normal mouse, all the offspring are normal. This is technically expressed by saying that the waltzing character is recessive, while normality is dominant; but one cannot tell beforehand whether a given character will be dominant or recessive. When the hybrid, apparently quite normal, mice are inbred, their offspring show 25 per cent. of pure waltzers and 75 of normals. If these waltzers of the second filial generation are bred with others like themselves, they produce only pure waltzers. If the normals of the second filial generation are bred with others like themselves, a third of them will produce pure normals, but the other two-thirds will produce normals and waltzers in the previous 3 : 1 ratio. One might sell one of the second filial waltzers as a pure waltzer, though its parents were normal, as also was one of its grandparents.

We may mention half-a-dozen examples of characters which show Mendelian inheritance, placing the dominant first in each case : hornlessness and the presence of horns in cattle ; normal hair and long Angora hair in rabbits and guinea-pigs ; crest and no crest in poultry ; bandless shells and banded shells in the woodsnail ; tallness and dwarfness in peas ; susceptibility to rust and immunity from this disease in wheat. But no one knows why one character should be dominant and another recessive.

SHUFFLING THE HEREDITARY CARDS.

At the beginning of each individual life, when

the egg-cell is fertilised, a usually equal number of hereditary items is contributed by each parent. If one of the parents has a dominant character, like a tendency to early cataract, which the other parent has not, the unfortunate probability is that the offspring will show the dominant character. Mendel supposed that the offspring produced in equal numbers two kinds of germ-cells, one contingent with, and the other contingent without, the factor or gene for the dominant character. Now, if the said offspring should marry another with similar history, the likelihood is that three-fourths of the grandchildren would show the tendency to early cataract. There is an inexorable shuffling of the hereditary cards before the making of each new " hand."

There may be other modes of inheritance besides the Mendelian mode. Thus blending may occur in some cases. But every year sees a further demonstration of Mendelism, and the discovery has put into the hands of breeders and cultivators a method by which desired results can be reached both quickly and surely. Heredity has made a great stride towards becoming an exact science.

V

THE EVOLUTION OF MAN

WHAT Darwin argued for was the solidarity of man with the rest of creation. He showed us the rock whence we were hewn, the pit whence we were digged. So far as it can be proved, he proved man's affiliation with an anthropoid or ape-like stock. Man is bound to the mammalian order of Primates (monkeys and apes) by an all-pervading similitude of structure, by his museum of bodily relics, by the way in which he climbs up his presumed genealogical tree during embryonic development, by his frequent untoward slips down some of the rungs on the steep ladder of evolution, by sharing certain diseases and parasites, and by the harmonious mingling of his blood with that of the higher apes.

DARWIN'S CONCLUSIONS.

Thus at the end of " The Descent of Man " Darwin wrote : " We must, however, acknowledge, as it seems to me, that man, with all his noble qualities, with sympathy which feels for the most debased, with benevolence which extends not only to other men, but to the humblest living creature, with his God-like intellect, which has penetrated into the movements and constitution of the solar system—with all these exalted powers—man still bears in his bodily frame the indelible stamp of his lowly origin."

In many cases the repulsion to the Darwinian conclusion has an æsthetic basis. "What a piece of work is a man"; how could he be a distant cousin of an ape? But those who ask this question should ask another: How can he be a much nearer cousin of a Bushman? And what of the individual ascent of the greatest as well as the least from a single cell and an unprepossessing embryo? It does not affect our estimate of Shakespeare that he was once a silly child. Newton was ushered into the world as one of the miserablest of infants, and yet we feel no difficulty in agreeing with the poet :—

> "Nature and Nature's laws lay dark as night !
> God said, Let Newton be, and all was light !"

The repulsion is partly based on misunderstanding, for it is the way of many to be hasty. They do not take the trouble to understand, that no one supposes man to have been derived from any existing simians. According to the scientific view man is a scion of a stock common to him and the higher apes, the divergence of humanoid and anthropoid occurring, perhaps, a million or more years ago ! Furthermore, if the æsthetes were aware of the reasonableness of chimpanzees, gorillas, and orangs—take the simple case of discovering the use of a lever and making other levers on a different scale—they might be less inclined to be ashamed of their poor relations.

PHILOSOPHICAL REVOLT.

When we speak to wise men about the arboreal apprenticeship of man's ancestors, we often detect a broad smile—which sometimes becomes audible. This is not due to a scientific scepticism, for which there is much to be said, as to whether man's ancestors did actually pass through an arboreal phase ; it expresses philosophical incredulity. To suppose that man, who sends his tendrils to the stars, who ponders over his origin and destiny, who bends Nature to his will, should have emerged from a monkeyish race, what absurdity ! Man is in his being too far apart from mammals to be thought of as solidary with them in his becoming. But if man was not evolved from a Primate stock, the only alternative is to believe that he arose, as regards his higher self at least, in a manner which

is indescribable in scientific terms. This aban-
donment of the scientific problem seems premature, and it jettisons continuity to preserve a
dubious dignity. One cannot, indeed, think too
highly of man, but if he is so great an achievement
then there must have been the right stuff in those
creatures from whom he arose.

APES AND APE-MEN.

Somewhere or other, perhaps in Egypt, in the
Oligocene Period, there was a divergence of the
Anthropoid apes from the stock of the Old
World monkeys—another great cleavage. These
early Anthropoids went roving far and wide in
Africa, Europe, and Asia, just as their simian
ancestors had done. A million or more years ago,
in the middle of the Miocene Period, and probably in Northern India, the human family
parted company with the giant apes, which continued on paths of their own, leading to the
orangs, chimpanzees, and gorillas of to-day.
But the human family had a long way to travel
before man emerged ; and there are indications
of a succession of " tentative men "—somewhat
shadowy beings, it must be confessed, so frag-
mentary are the remains from which they have
been rehabilitated. Lowest is Hesperopithecus,
the ape-man of the Western World, represented
by *a single tooth* from the Lower Pliocene of

Nebraska ! It seems incautious to base any large conclusion on a single tooth. But if the ape-man of Nebraska is valid, it would be interesting to know how he got there, this early traveller—so far from the Asiatic cradle of his race.

TENTATIVE MEN.

In an authoritative work like Sir Arthur Keith's " Antiquity of Man " (Second Edition, London, 1924) we may read the thrilling story of various tentative men, Hominid but not Homo. The two most important were Pithe-canthropus the Erect, fragmentarily represented in Java, and Eoanthropus of the Sussex Weald, the possessor of the Piltdown skull.

To these must be added the treasure that Professor Raymond Dart found at Taungs, eighty miles north of Kimberley, in Bechuana-land. It was among other related fossils in a limestone rock, about fifty feet below the surface. It consisted of the face bones and the cast of a skull. Among its features may be mentioned the non-receding forehead, the absence of pro-minent eyebrow ridges, and the humanoid appearance of the lower part of the face. The teeth, which seem to be those of the first or milk set, also show distinct approximations to our own. It is argued that *Australopithecus africanus*, as the creature has been called, carried his head high, and did not slouch so much as do living apes. There is evidence of a respectably large brain; but some slight deficiency in this respect, as compared with a gorilla for instance, may be due to the fact that the individual fortuitously preserved had not reached the years of discretion.

The tentative conclusion is that the Taungs skull is intermediate between Anthropoids and Hominids, that it may well belong to the stock ancestral to both. It has more humanoid features than the skull of any other Anthropoid. It is a welcome link in a growing chain, and even if a mistake be made here and there, it is not the case in these matters that the chain has only the strength of its weakest link.

How untrue it is to speak as if all the evolution-links in man's pedigree were missing! The wonder is that we know so many. As their number grows it will probably be found that there are several collateral lines, as is known to be the case with the fine array of fossil horses. All the known stages that make such a fine gradation of equine evolution are not on the same line. There were several equine lines, only one of which led to our modern horse.

In the same way it is already clear that there were several Hominid lines, only one of which led on to the modern man type. But these

I 2

tentative men, like Pithecanthropus and Eoanthropus, are of great interest in indicating the
steps in the evolution, even though they or some
of them may be off the main line of advance.
The discovery of several humanoid antiques in a
comparatively short time leads one to expect
many other " finds."

MAN AT LAST.

The earliest-known species of the genus Homo
is the Heidelberg man ; then came the Rhodesian
man ; and long after him the men of the
Neanderthal. None of these was *directly*
ancestral to us ; they were collateral offshoots
on lines of their own ; they belonged to the
genus Homo, not to the species *Homo sapiens ;*
they shared in the struggle but did not enter into
the promises. At last came " the man-child
glorious," as Emerson calls him somewhat
flatteringly, diverging into the races we know—
Australian, Negro, Mongol, Alpine, Medi-
terranean, and Nordic. The reduction of the
black pigment, which the human family shares
with gorilla and chimpanzee, is carried farthest
in the Nordic Race—certainly the blondest of
mankind, yet not without a number of primitive
traits.

TENTATIVE MEN.

Perhaps the philosophers who smile at the

anthropologist's efforts do not sufficiently realise the sublimity of the long process whereby from the Primate stem there diverged a succession of branches : first, the branch of New World monkeys ; second, the branch of Old World monkeys ; third, the branch of small apes or gibbons ; fourth, the branch of the larger anthropoid apes ; and fifth, the branch of Hominidæ. The monkeys as we know them did not lead on to apes, but there was an ancestral stem which split into the monkey-line and the ape-line. Similarly, apes as we know them did not lead on to man, but there was a generalised anthropoid stem which split into the relatively non-progressive modern apes and the relatively progressive Hominidæ. Moreover, there were, as we have seen, various Hominidæ before there was Homo, all shadowy figures unfortunately, yet indicative of *tentative men.*

And even when Homo had emerged, did not the sifting-out process continue ?—for it is generally believed that the Neanderthal man, who was truly human—a skilled artificer, using fire, reverently burying his dead—was a collateral and no ancestor of ours. The dimly descried history—for the inquiry is still young—gives one the impression of tentative apes and tentative men, of ages of experiment and sifting, of a candelabra-like branching of the genealogical tree. All who envisage the facts clearly must resent the vulgarity of the half-truth that " man sprang from monkeys." To many, who are willing to pass beyond scientific description to philosophical or religious interpretation, it is impossible to shut out the idea of an inherent purpose as the core of the evolution-process. And why should we try to shut it out ?

WHAT OF THE MISSING LINK ?

We cannot suppose that man, as we know him now, emerged suddenly in a non-human family ; but it is quite in line with what we know to occur to-day to suppose that the evolution of the distinctive human qualities, say of intellect and language, included mutations—that is to say, abrupt or brusque new departures. Evolution seems to be in many cases saltatory—a great advance is made at a stride. The Proteus leaps as well as creeps. Just as we recognise to-day the occasional appearance of a genius, so it is quite scientific to suppose that mutations occurred in the ascent of man. We do not understand the conditions leading to mutations, but we know that mutations occur, and that they usually have great staying power.

It must be admitted that the missing link is still missing. In other words, no extinct type is as yet known which can be regarded as the

common ancestor of Hominidæ and the higher
anthropoid apes. On the other hand, as we have
mentioned, there are several extinct creatures
like Pithecanthropus which must be regarded as
humanoid, though not of the modern man type.
It should be needless to say that there is no
question of any ape " becoming a man," as it is
expressed by those who do not understand what
organic evolution means. A rock-dove does not
become a fantail, or a crab-apple a Golden
Pippin. From the generalised base of the
Anthropoid Ape branch there diverged another
branch of humanoids; one of the twigs of this
branch was Homo, and a secondary twig was
Homo sapiens. And there never was a first man,
any more than a first wheat or a first horse. By
changes and siftings certain humanoids gradually gave rise to men ; by changes and siftings
certain men gradually gave rise to *Homo sapiens*.

FACTORS IN MAN'S ASCENT.

The soundest objection to the Darwinian
theory of the ascent of man is that while it
indicates a mode of origin, it leaves us wondering
how it all came about. In other words, we do
not as yet know very much about the factors that
operated in man's emergence. We have not got
beyond such suggestions as the following :—Man
belongs to an order which was moving in the

direction of improved brains, more words, and increased gregariousness. In Miocene times, when humanoids were separating off from anthropoids, great cerebral advances were being made, we know not why, in other orders of mammals, such as the elephants. Whatever may have been the stimulus, it was cerebral advance that particularly marked the Primate, the simian, the anthropoid, and the humanoid stocks. There is no special difficulty in the fact that man progressed much more than his collaterals ; this phenomenon occurs all through organic evolution.

A MOMENTOUS DESCENT.

Perhaps the fact that man's ancestors probably came down from the trees, while the monkeys and apes remained arboreal, may have been momentous ; perhaps we may lay emphasis on the erect attitude and the correlated increase in the power of speech ; perhaps there was great significance in the relative lack of physical strength, the prolonged antenatal life, infancy, and childhood, the growing sociality and kindliness. These factors work in virtuous circles. Strong kin-sympathy favours sociality and is enhanced by it ; improved brains favour language and have their capacity augmented by it ; parental care makes a long infancy possible and the prolonged infancy favours the development of gentleness in the individual and its evolution in the race. Modern research is leading us away from the picture of primitive men as brutish, dull, lascivious, and bellicose. There is more justification for regarding primitive men as clever and kindly, adventurous and inventive.

BRAIN-STRETCHING.

Professor Elliot Smith, one of the most distinguished of evolutionary anatomists, regards man as the outcome of a well-defined variational trend of brain-development—the differentiation of the neo-pallium—which began as far back as the tree-shrews and the Tarsioids. There may have been mutations or brusque advances, like that which led to the emergence of Homo among humanoids, or of *Homo sapiens* among Homines ; but behind these was a steady and persistent evolution of the brain along a well-defined course, in which the emphasis was increasingly laid on the capacity of the brain for visualising on the one hand, and for controlling dexterity on the other.

EYES AGAINST NOSE.

In the evolutionary history of animal races there are many examples of steady advance along a definite line ; and the same was probably true in the emergence of man. He shook off the lien of the past with its going on " all fours," its sniffing and nosing, its fumblings and inattentiveness. He evolved along a line marked by improvements in visualising powers and in manipulative dexterity, and by the outgrowth of a pre-frontal cerebral area which had to do with focussing attention and controlling mental processes. Correlated with these and the growth of kin-sympathy was the development of the art of speech, in which words are used as counters in thinking-experiments, as aids in social life, and as tokens in that mutual corroboration which is the beginning of science.

One of the most impressive diagrams ever published is that in which Professor Elliot Smith compares the brains of tree-shrew, tarsier, and marmoset, and shows the gradual reduction of the olfactory region, and the gradual predominance of the centres for vision, hearing, touch, dexterity, attention, and the unifying of the brain. And what is true of the marmoset, the most primitive of living monkeys, is still more striking for the higher apes, and for man most of all. The comparison of the worst human brain ever recorded with the largest known gorilla's brain shows us how much we have to be thankful for ! Success has been to the visualisers.

This familiar phrase is not always used in the same sense. Some use it in reference to the momentous divergence of the human or Hominid lineage from that of the Anthropoid Apes.

Then there are others who use the phrase " antiquity of man " to refer to *the first sure signs* of the presence of the modern type of man, and these sure signs take us back to only some 20,000 years—to deposits in the latter third of the Pleistocene period. But this is unsatisfactory, since there are " Eolithic implements," believed by many to be of human workmanship, which lie in what are regarded as Pliocene deposits, dating provisionally from 300,000 or 350,000 years ago. Moreover, we cannot dream of accepting any such recentness as 20,000 years, when we think of the great diversity of black, brown, yellow, and white races. We must allow time for the splitting of the common stock into types so divergent as a fair European, a representative Chinaman, and a full-blooded Negro. We must also allow time for the rise and decline of the collateral species of Neanderthal man, who was a Homo, though no ancestor of ours.

Thirdly, we use the phrase " the antiquity of man," as Sir Arthur Keith does in his great book, for the time when the brain of man reached a human level or standard, say of an average capacity of 1,000 cubic centimetres, and then " we have reasonable grounds for presuming that man was approaching the human standard in size of brain by the commencement of the Pliocene period." But this probably means about 500,000 years ago—a great age !

MAN STILL EVOLVING.

There must have been a common stem of *Homo sapiens* from which arose the branches which we know as Negroes, Negroids, Australoids, Mongoloids, and Europeans. Unfortunately, the early Pleistocene ancestral type from which these collateral branches might have arisen has not yet been found ; and long before this, in the Pliocene, we must look for a common ancestral type from which arose the modern man type, the Piltdowner, and the men of Neanderthal. It is difficult for us to picture such antiquity. Even if we take a moderate estimate of the duration of the Pleistocene period, say 200,000 years, that means, if we allow four generations to the century, that " man's body has been renewed some 8,000 times since the dawn of the Pleistocene." What a sublimely long ascent we have behind us ! But, as Sir Arthur Keith points out, it is not less important to realise that " the drama of man's evolution is still proceeding in our slums, country cottages, and palaces, just as it did in the days when man's only roof was the wide dome of the sky." In a very real sense we are still in the Garden of Eden ; but, alas, the serpent still lurks among the trees !

THE GARDEN OF EDEN.

An interesting general result is that primitive man must have spread in very early days all the world over. " For in reality the Garden of Eden was world-wide. Even England was part of it—apparently an important part. So were the continent of Europe and the ancient lands of Egypt and Mesopotamia. Our search shows that it extended to the most distant lands of Africa, Australia, Asia, and America." We do not suppose that Sir Arthur Keith means that the cerebral mutation that set man on his feet occurred many times over in different parts of the earth—it was surely too wonderful for that ! He means, we take it, that man's coming to his own, though marked by occasional leaps of light, was on the whole a gradual dawn. He means that the evolution was not confined to " a single sunlit idyllic glade," but continued for ages over a wide arena and with many a temporary defeat.

Pithecanthropus was found in Java, the Piltdown man lived in Sussex, the Rhodesian man was far away in South Africa, the Neanderthal man was widespread in Europe, there are rumours of strange primitive half-Simian, half-Hominid creatures being discovered in Egypt, and now comes Australopithecus from Bechuana-land! No one can be sure as yet where *Homo sapiens* actually emerged, but it looks as if tentative Hominids, among whom Professor Dart's discovery may have to be ranked, and tentative men like Pithecanthropus and the Piltdowner, had a very widespread outcrop. Emerson's " Song of Nature " rings in our ears :

> " Twice I have moulded an image,
>   And thrice outstretched my hand,
>   Made one of day, and one of night,
>   And one of the salt sea-sand.

Tentative Hominids, tentative men, tentative wise men (*Homo sapiens*) :

> " His couriers come by squadrons,
>   He comes not to the gate."

PIONEERS OF MANKIND.

How many couriers, from Pithecanthropus of Java to Australopithecus of Taungs ? and the wide geographical distribution of these interesting emergences shows us the wisdom of Sir Arthur Keith's remark : " In reality the Garden of Eden was world-wide ; and its drama is still unfinished." In our midst to-day there may be Mutations emerging, destined to take the place of *Homo sapiens*, just as he took that of Neanderthal man.

Is man an animal? What a bad pseudo-question! Is a bird a reptile because the queen of the air evolved from an earthbound Dinosaur? For man, certainly not of the order of Melchisedec, who was "without descent or pedigree," arose as an emergence or mutation, a new creative synthesis, from a Primate stock of which, though he transcended it in reasonable discourse and much else, he has no reason to be ashamed. To a cheering fact the relics of "tentative men" bear witness : that behind us there is not a descent, but an *ascent*. Long may it continue !

THE EVOLUTION OF MIND.

Sir Isaac Newton was once an infant crying in the night. Whence came his mind that leaped from the falling apple to the distant star ? No doubt the transcendental answer that we have already quoted is true : " God said, Let Newton be, and all was light " ; but it is not a scientific answer. We know that Newton's mind emerged in the process of continuous development from an egg-cell, so small that 700 of them could be laid side by side on a line an inch long. This egg-cell consisted, from the chemist's outlook, of a great complexity of proteins and other carbon-compounds, but in terms of these by no trick of words can mind be explained. All that we can say is that the egg-cell has an implicit mental aspect, which will emerge into activity when the material conditions are suitable. And the mental aspect, like the bodily, is the resultant of a multitude of ancestral components.

THE BEGINNINGS OF THINGS.

The evolutionist traces man's pedigree back to a mammalian stock common to him and to the higher apes ; he derives mammals from reptiles, and reptiles from amphibians, and amphibians from fishes. Thus he works back and back to the simplest forms of life ; and these, if he is daring and consistent, he derives from the dust of the earth. But the earth in turn he traces back, by one theory or another, to a whirling nebular mass of which our sun is the condensed centre.

Was there mind in the nebula? We have only to change the question into : Was there *life* in the nebula ? to see that it is wrongly put. All that the thoroughgoing evolutionist can say is that our solar-system-nebula was a fragment of reality which contained within it the promise and potency of that aspect of reality which we know in higher animals and in ourselves as

" mind." In this sense we may scientifically say : In the beginning was mind. We must not think of " matter " as a sort of irreducible bedrock whence all has been hewn ; it is but an aspect of that bedrock, an aspect which we catch sight of by using certain scientific methods.

In short, " matter " is an abstraction, and so is " mind." To say that matter has given origin to mind is an outworn confusion of thought ; yet to say that the human mind has made " matter " seems again a dangerous half-truth. For the " mind " *that we scientifically know at present* is associated with a living organism which is likewise " matter."

THREE CERTAINTIES.

Our nervous system is a scientific actuality that can be measured and weighed ; it is complex beyond our power of picturing ; there are in our fore-brain more than five times as many nerve-cells as there are people living on the earth ; the inter-related activities baffle our imagination. Now, any theoretical view that disregards this material, bodily, neural, metabolic aspect must be wrong.

On the other hand, what we are surest about is the reality of our inner life of consciousness, our thoughts and feelings, desires and purposes. No doubt the unconscious is a very powerful factor—that is another question ; but what counts for more than anything else, for a day, a month, a year, or a lifetime, is often our imponderable *purpose*. Therefore, any theoretical view that disregards this mental, psychical, subjective aspect must be wrong.

But the third certainty is that these two aspects—body and mind, cerebral and conscious, neurosis and psychosis, objective and subjective, are very closely wrapped up together in everyday life. If there is a relation between the two, there is nothing to which we can compare it ; if we have to do with a unity, it is equally unique. We are often mind-BODIES, as when we are tramping along the weary road, but how our steps are lightened by the good news we hear from the friend we meet ! We are often body-MINDS, as in our pensive mood, but our pulse changes with our thoughts and our emotions evoke chemical messengers from the recesses of our ductless glands !

Thus every theoretical view must be wrong that ignores the close interdependence between the protoplasmic organism and the psychical personality.

THE DIRIGIBLE DOG.

The well-known inventor, Mr. J. H. Hammond, made a " dirigible dog " with selenium eyes which controlled the steering of a driving motor in his hinder parts. If a hand flashlight be turned on the eyes, the " dog " will follow it round the room at a speed of about 3 feet per second. If the light be switched off, then the " dog " stops ; but if the light be turned on again the contraption will resume its pursuit and will continue as long as the light reaches the condensing lenses in sufficient intensity. The mechanism adjusts itself automatically so that the two lenses are equally illumined. In its following " it is more faithful than the proverbial ass behind the bucket of oats. To the uninitiated the performance of the pseudo-dog is very uncanny indeed."

There are some who think of real dogs in this mechanical way, and delude themselves into the belief that the machine-theory suffices to describe life. But while there are many automatisms in animals and even in man, a machine cannot elaborate a theory that it is a machine ! If we must theorise over what may be a limiting problem for the human intelligence, we must choose between the *dualist* view that our inmost self uses the nervous system as the musician his instrument, and the *monist* view that the psychical and the nervous activities are inseparable aspects of the living creature, like the two sides of a shield, or like the concave and the convex surfaces of a dome. There are great authorities behind the two theories and great difficulties in front of them. The important practical *fact* is that both aspects are real in the here and the now.

IS MAN'S EVOLUTION GOING ON?

Evolution is an organic racial change in a definite direction or in several definite directions, and there is a strong probability that it is still continuing in mankind. Why this caution of statement ? There is obviously considerable change from generation to generation, but most of this is outside the living body and only repercusses indirectly, if at all, on the flesh and blood constitution. The medical student is well aware of the minor variations that are always cropping up in man's bodily frame, but only in a few cases is there any indication that these are taking *racial grip*. The period of exact observation is short. Mental mutations in the way of talent and originality are not uncommon, but their effect on the race is oftener indirect than germplasmic. Many animal species in the past seem to have continued for ages in a state of equilibrium—neither advancing nor retrogressing; it is possible that man may be at present resting after his ascent. Moreover, if mankind is at present evolving, it must not be assumed that the direction of the change is progressive. For evolution is sometimes retrogressive. Perhaps man illustrates something of both—retrogressing, for instance, as regards his little toe and progressing as regards cerebral complexity. In any case we must not assume too facilely that man is at present evolving or that the direction of his continued evolution is all that we might wish.

Of our past history (as already recognised) we carry about a museum of relics, like the dwindled third eyelid, the rarely useable muscles of the ear, and the vermiform appendix. We know a great deal about these vestiges, some of which are apt to be troublesome, but we know very little about *incipient structures*, which might be compared to buds that have still to open. The hand of the past is much more readily discerned than the promise of the future. Let us accept, however, the probability that human evolution continues, and inquire into its trend.

RACES NO LONGER MULTIPLYING.

One of the common results of evolution is a diversity of kinds. What a multitude of different brambles and willows, snails and mice ! So it was with man in early days, for within the species *Homo sapiens* there are at least a score of very distinctive races. Can one say that this kind of evolution continues in mankind ? The answer must be in the negative. Isolating barriers have been largely removed ; pure races are few. In a locality like Sicily we find a puzzling blend of Greeks, Latins, Saracens, Normans, and Africans ; and many another country is a racial melting-pot. When marked variations crop up, let us say in the direction of musical talent, it is always possible theoretically to start a caste, like a breed among domesticated animals, by the mating of similars. But this sort of thing is not occurring to-day.

IS MAN'S BODY BECOMING MORE PERFECT ?

Another familiar result of evolution is increasingly perfect adaptation, but it is doubtful if there are many examples of this in present-day mankind. Perhaps there is a tendency to a reduction of the wisdom-teeth, which sometimes do not show themselves at all, and this might be an adaptation if it meant that there was more room for the others. But there are few cases like this. Perhaps there is a tendency to a dwindling of the little toe, which might mean a slight economy, though it could hardly be called a positive adaptation. It seems very probable that the length of our food-canal, 30 feet or so, is an anachronism, far too long for the punctual meals and fine food of to-day, but it is very difficult to prove that it is becoming shorter Man's body is indeed a bundle of adaptations or fitnesses, but our point is that there is not much evidence of additions being made. It must be remembered, however, that the precise recording of variations is a relatively recent scientific habit, and that man has great ingenuity in securing *artificial* adaptations. But we must also realise that under modern conditions the processes of selection are rarely stringent enough or consistent enough to secure the persistence of useful changes even when they crop up. It is so relatively easy for people with misadaptations, such as short sight, to survive and flourish, that the danger is that man may lose some of his hard-won gains. Perhaps, however, we may find an instance of positive adaptation at present in progress in the increasing immunity that certain races show to some common diseases.

A third result of evolution is increased complexity of bodily structure, but it does not seem that modern man shows much evidence of progress along this line. Perhaps his body has already attained to such a balanced complexity that few big changes can be looked for. Perhaps we should rather expect simplification, as in the number of teeth ; and here again it must be kept in mind that throwing off the yoke of

Natural Selection as much as man has done, without replacing it by rational methods of sifting, is apt to spell retrogression. This is the more serious because man can artificially save himself from natural penalties. Some authorities believe that baldness is a constitutional variation among men, which is markedly on the increase in certain places and stocks. If we accept this view, for the sake of argument, we have an instance of a change which would probably be fatal in Wild Nature, whereas in conditions of civilised urbanity it merely means a very economical way of wearing the hair. Even if Natural Selection were operative, its sifting could be circumvented by the purchase of a wig.

INCREASING COMPLEXITY OF BRAIN.

Another consideration is this. Many parts of our body are highly specialised, but some remained generalised, and therefore on general grounds open to evolution. But in cases like the hand, which remains very generalised, it is plain that there is survival value in its remaining in this condition—able to do anything, a universal tool. But there is one line of complexifying which is almost certainly open, and that is an increase in the intricacy of inter-relations among the nerve-cells of the cerebral cortex. It seems that the average size of the human brain has not increased since the time of the Cro-Magnons, who lived perhaps 20,000 years ago ; but it is quite consistent with this that there should be a complexifying of linkages among the 9,200,000,000 nerve-cells of the cerebral cortex. The linkages probably increase in our lifetime of intelligent behaviour and thinking ; it may be that there is a racial change in the same direction. It is the kind of variation that would pay in modern life. It is the kind of variation that would be fostered by the environment afforded in a civilised community.

Another promiseful line of change in man's constitution is an alteration in the relative length of the various periods of life. When we compare different kinds of life-history among animals we find that some have a long youth and a short maturity ; that others have a telescoped youth, being born almost grown-up ; that others have a very long adolescence and almost no senescence, and so on. Now, there is some evidence that one of the biological changes in progress in mankind is a lengthening out of the youthful period. At present this may be largely ascribed to individual changes of habit ; but it may be that there is also an organic racial movement in the same direction. It is not difficult to see that this might come about by variations in the endocrinal or regulatory system.

UNIQUENESS OF MAN.

Apart from man's power of conceptual inference (or reason), his power of language, and his way of regulating his conduct by the light and warmth of ideas, the greatest difference between him and animals is the paramount importance of the social heritage. The trend of evolution which is most certain is not on the organismal line at all ; it consists in the enrichment and increased utilisation of the social heritage—literature, art, institutions, stored knowledge, traditions, and unwritten laws. Man is indeed the long result of time ; but the change that is coming about, behind all the details of eugenics, eutechnics, eutopias, and eupsychics, is the growing conviction that we can in some measure control the future evolution of our race. This is the line of advance. *In hoc signo laboremus.*

VI

THREE KINDS OF EVOLUTION

PEOPLE do not grumble over the number of technical terms connected with a yacht or a motor car, yet they reproach science for having so many. The reason for technical terms is mainly that a new thing or a new idea requires a new name. It wastes time and destroys clearness when the same word is used in several different senses. How much confusion there has been over words like " force " or " value," to take two familiar examples. The word " evolution " is another of these overworked words. It is applied to different processes which have little in common except that they are processes of change or of Becoming. Science suffers more from having too few words than from having too many. Let us illustrate this in reference to evolution.

AN OVER-WORKED WORD.

We hear of the evolution of stars, of the solar

system, of the earth, of scenery, of climates, of minerals, of the chemical elements. People who should know better speak of the evolution of the frog when they mean its development, for organic evolution has to do with racial transformation and affiliation (phylogeny), not with individual development, *e.g.*, from the egg-cell to the embryo, from the larva to the adult (ontogeny). We hear, rightly enough, of the evolution of species, types, classes, and even faunas or floras ; but we hear also of the evolution of warm-bloodedness or the evolution of the nervous system, or of sex. We hear of the evolution of animal behaviour, including instincts and intelligence. We sometimes hear of the evolution of consciousness and mind. The evolution of man is a right usage, if we mean his ascent from an ancestral stock common to the higher Anthropoid apes and the early "tentative men." But a different note is sounded when people speak of the evolution of language, of ideas, of art, of music, of social institutions, of religions. We even hear of the evolution of evolution theories. Such a diversified usage is rather disconcerting. It cannot be the same process of Evolution in such a variety of fields. Perhaps we may distinguish to advantage three different kinds of evolution.

154

It used to be a favourite exercise—almost an intellectual game—to compare a human Society to an organism. The individuals were compared to the cells of the body ; aggregates, like streets of storehouses or shipping offices, were compared to tissues ; integrates, like municipal buildings or hospitals or cleansing departments, were compared to organs. The Government was likened to the nervous system and the producers were compared with muscles. But this pleasing analogy has little value, since the truly scientific comparison is between human societies and animal " societies," such as bee-hive and ant-hill, rookery and beaver-village.

No doubt the changes in human societary forms have some resemblance to organic evolution among non-social forms. New departures arise in both cases—social variations and organic variations. There is sifting in both cases, social selection and natural selection, and the latter overlaps the former, though in a decreasing degree. In both cases there are influential processes of isolation and segregation. There is also what may be called social heredity—a relation of continuity between successive generations apart from that which is sustained by the germ-plasm. It seems, then, that there is an interesting analogy between evolution in the world of ordinary organisms and evolution in human societies. But are not the differences greater than the resemblances?

UNIQUENESS OF SOCIAL EVOLUTION.

What are the new features that separate social evolution from organic evolution? To some extent they are implied in the apartness of man —who has language, a power of working with general ideas (reason), a vivid self-consciousness, and some historical sense. He thinks of past and future in a new way, for there is formed in his mind a conceptual purpose—something very much more than a vivid mental image, such as some quick-brained mammals probably have.

We must avoid thinking of Man as an intellectual and moral Melchisedec; he has his affiliations, as we have seen. Yet we must recognise that when man came to himself, he made all things new. No animal, not even the most intelligent, gives more than hints of " general ideas "; no animal, not even a parrot, expresses a judgment or makes a simple sentence. Animals have many virtues, but we can hardly suppose that they ever think of their behaviour in relation to an ideal—they have not more than the raw materials of ethical conduct. In many cases, or at many times, no doubt, man does not rise from intelligence to reason, or from behaviour to conduct, but he always has this power or potentiality.

THE SOCIAL HERITAGE.

Another great difference, however, is in the extent to which the *extra-organismal* inheritance counts in human society. There is a registration of past history outside the living individual —in traditions and customs, conventions and laws, in literature and art, in institutions and permanent products. Man's mind is made as well as born, and it is fashioned in no small measure by the " social heritage," which some would call the " social environment." If the natural inheritance of flesh and blood be called fundamental, even in mankind, the social heritage may be ranked supreme. But it must not be thought of as always working for good. Many of the best efforts of reformers lose much of their fruition because of antipathetic factors in our social heritage from the early industrial or " palæotechnic " age.

No doubt there are slight anticipations of the human social heritage among social or gregarious animals where there are permanent products continued on from generation to generation, as in the bee-hive, the ant-hill, the termitary, or the beaver-dam. But important as these are, they are only adumbrations.

In his " Instincts of the Herd," Dr. William Trotter pointed out very clearly that one of the differences between social and individualistic life is that the society acts as a shield which automatically shelters individual variations. Under the shield of a society, with its division of labour and its social sentiment, it is possible for individuals to survive who would soon have been eliminated if they had lived alone. The halt, the lame and the blind are sheltered ; the unpractical and the absent-minded are shielded ; and it is easy to give good reasons why this should continue, but there can be no escape from penalties whenever Society shelters the unsound to the extent of allowing them to multiply. What escape can there be from Herbert Spencer's " dilemma of civilisation " : " Any arrangements which, in a considerable degree, prevent superiority from profiting by the rewards of superiority, or shield inferiority from the evils it entails ; any arrangements that make it as well to be inferior as to be superior, are arrangements diametrically opposed to the progress of organisation, and the reaching of a higher life " ? We cannot read these wise words too often.

To a very large extent Man has rebelled against Nature's Sifting, and could not do otherwise. The danger lies in the fact that he has not yet substituted for Natural Selection a thought-out, firm, and consistent policy of rational and social selection. There is, indeed, no end of social selection, but it is too often of the kind that advertises for a gardener " without encumbrances," too often of the kind that lets the artist and the musician die, and condemns the eccentric mutation to celibacy. That way lies deterioration.

AN ILLUSTRATION FROM THE ANT-HILL.

In the ordinary course of Natural Selection there is keen individual struggle—of many kinds, but always *individual*. Of no organism can it be said that it lives or dies to itself, but its fate is, on the whole, in its own hands. It is penalised or rewarded according to its individual peculiarities. But whenever there is anything like a community or a society, the whole venue is changed. Thus there are soldier Termites which cannot feed themselves, and have to get their meals from the workers. There are slave-keeping ants which are not only quite unable to forage, but have to be spoon-fed by their slaves. And every one knows that drone-bees do not gather honey. These are extreme cases, but they illustrate one of the great differences between social and individualistic evolution, that the very fact of there being a society serves to shelter variants—not always progressive—which would be speedily eliminated under a non-social regime.

SELF-CONTROLLED EVOLUTION.

It is often said that Natural Selection works blindly, whereas Social Evolution is self-controlled. How far is this contrast true ? The usual Darwinian view is that if variations occur in an advantageous direction, then, other things equal, they will automatically lead the race or species in that direction. In cases where the juvenile mortality is enormous, those variants that have increased reproductivity will have most survivors after their kind, and quite automatically the species will move in a direction towards which it could not be said to be aiming —namely, towards greater fertility. The more fertile types will survive.

But this is only part of the truth. In a great many cases, especially among animals with good brains, the living creature shares in its own evolution. As we have said, it plays its hand of hereditary cards. It puts its talent out to usury. It trades with time and traffics with circumstance. If it has any little excellence, why, it uses it to advantage. It is selected by its environment, that is half of the truth ; but it may also select its environment. Animals are often purposive agents of great vigour, though there is probably none that adjusts its behaviour in reference to the light of a conceived purpose. That is man's prerogative.

It seems, therefore, that we should modify the sharpness of the contrast with which we started, and say that evolution in a human society often differs from that among animals, inasmuch as the human society, like the Great Man, often seeks *to make history*. It seeks to control itself in the light of a more or less luminous ideal.

THE SECOND KIND OF EVOLUTION.

Working from above downwards, we recognise as the second kind of evolution that which occurs among ordinary plants and animals. There is no hard and fast line of separation, especially when we keep in mind the bee-hive and the ant-hill, and other expressions of sociality among animals. There is a kind of animal sociology, and we cannot scout the idea of a plant sociology as absurd.

To obviate any suggestion of discontinuity, we must also remember that natural selection still operates to some extent in human society, for instance, in the case of diseases with a dif-ferential death-rate ; and that it operated much more markedly in bygone days. Even if we regard primitive man as intrinsically social, unable to stand alone, we must allow that the distinctive features of social evolution would be only incipient in the days of simple societary forms.

ORGANIC EVOLUTION.

Once more let us ask what has happened in organic evolution—in the evolution, let us say, of the single-toed modern horse and its relatives from the little primitive many-toed equine creatures of the early Eocene Ages. Just the same kind of process it was as we see to-day when man establishes a new breed of pigeons or poultry, a new variety of rose or chrysanthemum. With only one big difference, that, instead of Man, there was the System of Animate Nature with its manifold sifting and singling.

Novelties crop up, but not fortuitously, unless one would call the great variety of snow crystals "fortuitous." Tentatives are always being made and tested ; experiments are always being made, but many are futile. An organism sometimes changes itself by trying, but we cannot at present be sure that the direct bodily results of its trying are entailed. Perhaps what is usually continued from generation to generation in such cases is the tendency to try. It seems to us personally that what counts for most is the welling-forth of novelties from the arcana of the germ-cells.

A HINT FROM THE SLIPPER ANIMALCULE.

From generation to generation there is an emergence—often copious—of new permutations and combinations, and we wish, for a moment, to compare these to the remarkable periodic re-organisations that occur in the life-history of the Slipper Animalcule, Paramecium. This common Infusorian shows a periodic process called endomixis, in which the nuclear structures are scrapped and then re-organised, with results that spell *rejuvenation*. Professor Lorande Loss Woodruff and Miss Erdmann found that the process of endomixis occurs, in laboratory conditions, about once a month in a " pure line," that is to say, a lineage all descended from one—in this case, by division following division. Endomixis corresponds to the nuclear scrapping that occurs when two Slipper Animalcules come together to pool their resources and then re-divide them, to their presumed mutual advantage—a process known as conjugation. In a pure line, all descended from one, there is no conjugation, but there is this monthly process of scrapping and re-organising. Now this same process occurs in " wild " conditions in two very hardy and plastic species of Paramecium namely, *P. aurelia* and *P. caudatum*, and it seems to have the effect of rejuvenation. Now, no one would call a process like endomixis " accidental " or " fortuitous," in fact, it is as orderly as it is intricate. And our theory is that similar scrappings and re-organisations which are known to occur in the life-history of the germ cells, and others which are not yet known very definitely, may give rise to some of the variations and mutations that form the raw materials of progress.

THE TESTING OF TENTATIVES.

If we were asked to state as shortly as possible the most widely accepted theory of Organic Evolution, we should say " the testing of tentatives." But the tentatives are unconscious experiments in self-expression on the part of the implicit organisms called germ-cells, and the testing is effected in the clash of the struggle for existence, which often rises, however, into an endeavour after well-being. The novelties that crop up are, in many cases, obviously congruent with what has gone before, and cannot be called accidental. The testing in many cases is associated with the creature's will to live, and expresses an endeavour to play the hereditary cards to advantage. But in organic evolution the end worked towards is an immediate satisfaction in the concrete, whereas in social evolution the end worked towards is often the realisation of an abstract ideal, which may not have much to show for itself in the immediate here and now.

FEW ARE CHOSEN.

A distinctive feature of Organic Evolution, marking it off from Social Evolution and Inorganic Evolution, is the relentless elimination. Relatively few of those that are born are ever themselves able to reproduce. As Tennyson said : " Of fifty thousand seeds, she often brings but one to bear." There is terrible infantile mortality in mankind, even in civilised society, but it is trivial with what occurs in Nature. " So careful of the type she seems, so careless of the single life." Part of this elimination is quite indiscriminate and does not make for progress. It simply means that in certain cases the only organisms that have survived are those that work with a large margin. Sometimes, however, there is discriminate elimination ; the relatively fitter young forms survive ; and thus the species moves.

But there is another aspect to the sifting. In some cases there are conservative types, like the Lamp-Shell Lingula, which has lived on un changed for many millions of years. In some cases the new form flourishes alongside of the species from which it diverged. But in other cases the new displaces the old. There has been a continuous blotting out of species. Sometimes, indeed, an entire race, like that of the Flying Dragons or Pterodactyls, is lost, leaving no descendants whatsoever. A splendid race, " cast as rubbish to the void." Though they may have contributed indirectly to the System of Nature, they are wiped out as though they had not been. The old order changes, giving place to the new. Now there is very little like this when a nebula becomes a stellar system, or when thorium sinks down into lead. In short, it is characteristic of Organic Evolution that many individuals and groups of individuals that share in the struggle never enter into the promises. The process of *elimination* is distinctive.

IS ANYTHING INANIMATE?

If we use the word *history* for social evolution in mankind, and the term *Organic Evolution* for what has been true of plants and animals and of man as organism, then we might use some word like *genesis* for processes of Becoming that have taken place, and still take place, in the domain of the inorganic. There must be fallacy in using the same word " evolution " for the process of Becoming in fields so different as the Kingdom of Man, the Realm of Organisms, and the Domain of Things. Though there may not be any discontinuity, there are great differences between the Sociosphere, the Biosphere, and the Cosmosphere. Let us take a single instance of Genesis in the domain of the Inorganic— that is to say, apart from protoplasmic life and apart from what we ordinarily call mind. But he is a bold man who is quite sure that there is anything really *inanimate*.

THE EVOLUTION OF MATTER.

The discovery of radio-activity in 1896 led to a new view of matter and of the chemical elements. For the qualitative differences between different kinds of matter turn out to be fundamentally quantitative. The atom is comparable to a planetary system in which outer electrons (unit charges of negative electricity) circulate around a central body, which consists of inner electrons and a core of protons (unit charges of positive electricity). In the simplest atom, that of hydrogen, there is a single hydrogen-nucleus (usually regarded as equivalent to a proton), around which there revolves a single electron. The most complex known atom, that of uranium, consists of ninety-two electrons, revolving in orbits round the centre, and this centre is again a microcosm, consisting of 146 inner electrons and 238 hydrogen-nuclei or protons. The different elements form a system, the members of which, ninety-two less four or five gaps, differ from one another in the number and the orbits of the revolving electrons, and in the number of hydrogen-nuclei or protons. Matter seems to have been swallowed by electricity, and all the material universe is one. In other words, all matter is nothing but a manifestation of electricity.

But there is more to be said. Although man cannot control radio-active changes, either slowing or hastening them, he can watch them and see radio-active substances producing things different from themselves. The *unchangeableness* of matter has been disproved; the world is even more in flux than we thought. And this is an instance of inorganic genesis. Thus uranium may produce ionium, which produces radium. Or uranium may produce protactinium, which gives rise to actinium. From thorium may be produced lead, and from radium another lead, and from actinium yet another lead. There is an " evolution " of matter. But while there may be deep samenesses, there is no use in pretending that this is the same kind of evolution as that which we study in the Realm of Organisms, or in the Kingdom of Man.

VII

BECOMING, BEING, AND HAVING BEEN

MOST of us have enjoyed an autumn reverie in the harvest fields from which the sheaves have been gathered. We close our eyes and we see the ploughed field being sown ; we watch first the blade, then the ear, then the full corn in the ear ; then comes the harvesting, and the field is bare once more. The world is full of these beautiful cycles. Ringing almost everywhere in our ears are the old Hegelian words : BECOMING, BEING, and HAVING BEEN. We believe that if man were, for any unthinkable reason, to lose faith in the doctrine of evolution, he would immediately proceed to build up the idea afresh, for it has become organic in him to see everywhere a process of Becoming. There is " Werden und Vergehen," and then there is Weiter-Werden, becoming and disappearing and then becoming again.

How persistently this idea of cyclic change seems to have dwelt in Tennyson's mind :

> " There rolls the deep where grew the tree.
>   O earth, what changes hast thou seen !
> There, where the long street roars, hath been
>   The stillness of the central sea.
>
> The hills are shadows and they flow
>   From form to form, and nothing stands ;
> They melt like mist, the solid lands ;
>   Like clouds they shape themselves and go."

There is an old-fashioned poem by Rückert, called " Chidher," which we venture to quote from its translation in Dr. Theodor Merz's great " History of European Thought in the Nineteenth Century " (Vol. II., p. 289). It gives one in fine simplicity a vivid picture of the cyclic flux. As was said by the Greek philosopher Heraclitus : " All things flow."

> " Chidher, the ever youthful, spake,
>   I passed a city on my way,
> A man in a garden fruit did break,
> I asked him how long the town here lay ?
> He spoke, and broke on as before,
> ' The town stands ever on this shore,
> And will stand thus forevermore.'
>
> And when five hundred years were gone
> I came the same road as anon ;
> Then not a mark of town I met.
> A shepherd on a flute did play,

The cattle flower and foliage ate.
I asked how long is the town away?
He spake, and piped on as before,
'One plant is green when the other's o'er,
This is my pasture forevermore.'

And when five hundred years were gone
I came the same road as anon,
Then did I find with waves a lake,
A man the net cast in the bay,
And when he paused from his heavy take,
I asked since when the lake here lay?
He spake, and laughed my question o'er,
'As long as the waves break as of yore,
One fishes and fishes on the shore.'

And when five hundred years were gone
I came the same way as anon.
A wooded place I then did see,
And a hermit in a cell did stay;
He felled with an axe a mighty tree.
I asked since when the wood here lay?
He spake: 'The wood's a shelter forevermore,
I ever lived upon this floor,
And the trees will grow on as before.'

And when five hundred years were gone
I came the same way as anon,
But then I found a city filled
With market's clamour shrill and gay.
I asked how long is the city built,
Where's wood and sea and shepherd's play?
They pondered not my question o'er,
But cried: 'So was it long before,
And will go on forevermore.'
But when five hundred years are gone
I'll go the same way as anon."

THE CIRCULATION OF MATTER.

In one of our " Natural History Studies "
(Melrose, London, 1921) we have suggested the
dramatic value of the circulation of matter in the
system of Nature. " The rain falls ; the springs
are fed ; the streams are filled and flow to the
sea ; the mist rises from the deep and the clouds
are formed, which break again on the mountain-
side. The plant captures air, water, and salts,
and, with the sun's help, builds them up into
the bread of life. The animal eats the plant
and a new story begins. All flesh is in the long
run transformed grass. The animal becomes
part of another animal—another incarnation
begins. The silver cord of the bundle of life is
loosed, and earth returns to earth. The microbes
of decay break down the dead animal, and there
is a return to air, water, and salts. We may be
sure that nothing real is ever lost, neither of
matter nor of energy ; we are sure that all things
flow. Like Penelope in the Greek story, Nature
is continually unravelling her web and beginning
again. This is the circulation of matter, and
this is how the world goes round."

HUXLEY'S PICTURE OF CHANGE.

If we were making an anthology of scientific
prose, we should include this passage from
Huxley : " Natural knowledge tends more and

more to the conclusion that ' all the choir of heaven and furniture of the earth ' are the transitory forms of parcels of cosmic substance wending along the road of evolution, from nebulous potentiality, through endless growths of sun and planet and satellite ; through all varieties of matter ; through infinite diversities of life and thought ; possibly, through modes of being of which we neither have a conception, nor are competent to form any, back to the undefinable latency from which they arose. Thus the most obvious attribute of the cosmos is its impermanence. It assumes the aspect, not so much of a permanent entity, as of a changeful process, in which nought endures save the flow of energy and the rational order which pervades it."

What stories the geologists tell us of age-long breaking-down and building-up, disintegrations and re-integrations, scrapping and reconstruction, *Werden und Vergehen.* And when the geologists leave off, the cosmogonists begin with their account of the birth and death of stars, the cycle from nebula to nebula—an account so different from, and yet not incongruent with, Addison's thoughts when he wrote the familiar lines :—

" Soon as the ev'ning shades prevail,
The moon takes up the wondrous tale,

And, nightly to the list'ning earth,
Repeats the story of her birth."

How much the story has changed since Tenny-son wrote :—

> " They say
> The solid earth whereon we tread
> In tracts of fluent heat began,
> And grew to seeming random forms,
>
> The seeming prey of cyclic storms,
> Till at the last arose the man."

And we may also recall the fine lines from Psyche's lesson in *The Princess* :—

> " This world was once a fluid haze of light,
> Till toward the centre set the starry tides,
> And eddied into suns, that, wheeling, cast
> The planets."

"THE UNIVERSE. AS IT IS. AS IT WAS. AS IT WILL BE."

Some titles make one gasp, but surely the prize for that quality belongs to the last section of Dr. Herbert Dingle's fascinating book on " Modern Astrophysics " (London, 1924). The title of the section reads : " The Universe. As it is. As it was. As it will be." What supreme comprehensiveness ! How characteristic it is of man that his reach exceeds his grasp. As Dr. Dingle says : " The human mind, born too great for its ends, never at peace with its goal, is doomed ever to seek for that which it has not the power to attain." *Man has a passion for the asymptotic.*

THE UNIVERSE : AS IT IS.

It is easy to say these words ; but when we think for a moment we realise that we cannot really know the universe as it is. This is a popular delusion.

For suppose we attended our minds to the earth so as to know how *it* is, or a blade of grass is, at a given tick of the clock, " then we must wait eight and half minutes before we can say how the sun appeared at the same moment, because the light of the sun takes that time to reach our eyes." We read that when we see the star Spica of a night, we are really seeing it as it was 180 years ago, and that there are clusters in the sky which we observe by the light that left them long, long before the Christian Era began. It is plain, therefore, that we cannot know the Universe as it is.

We must not, of course, make too much of this limitation. When we say " the universe as it is," we mean " the universe as it appears." But this difference does not seem to be of great importance in connection, for instance, with the general shape and configuration of stellar systems, for these change with relative slowness compared with the velocity of light. It is another matter when we are comparing the physical states of near and distant bodies, for we are comparing them at different ages. What we see in the very distant star-cluster is not contemporaneous with what we see in Centauri, the nearest fixed star.

THE GALAXY.

It seems that the stellar universe is a finite flattened galaxy, in which the stars become less and less crowded, if we dare use such a word, with increasing distance in all directions. It might be compared to what we see when we walk out from a city on a very dark night ; the lamps become fewer and more distant as we pass into the country, where, at last, there are none. The total number of stars within the heavenly city and its suburbs—the whole galaxy, we mean—is estimated to be about 47 thousand millions.

Many, perhaps most, of these stars are double. Some of them are multiple. Many of them form systems, comparable to, though often different from, our solar system. These systems of stars show movements as wholes, as well as among their members. In other words, there seem to be great " stream movements " as well as revolutions. Even our own system, which occupies only a small corner in space, seems always to be leaving that corner behind, at the rate of hundreds of miles before we have finished this sentence, and yet without getting appreciably nearer that unknown goal which is called " the apex of the sun's way."

Another large fact is that the stars seem to pass through a life-cycle, from diffuseness to density, changing from red to yellow and then to white, and finally to red again in second childhood. Finally, perhaps, the star may become " dead " and dark—too faint, at least, to be visible.

THE SIZE OF THE UNIVERSE.

According to the cosmic measurers, the greatest diameter of the main mass of the universe, which lies symmetrically about the galactic plane, is about 100,000 " parsecs." And a " parsec " is about 19 million million miles. The origin of the unfamiliar word " parsec " is that a star at the distance of one parsec would have a *par*allax of one *sec*ond—hence *parsec*.

Instead of " parsec " we may use the unit " light year," that is to say, the distance which light, with a velocity of 186,300 miles per second, would travel in one year. A " light-year " is about a third (0·31) of a parsec. So that is quite plain.

177   M 2

The stars do not seem to differ very greatly from one another in the amount of material that they contain. As Professor Eddington says : " With few exceptions they range from half to five times the mass of the sun. There can no longer be serious doubt as to the general cause of this, although the details of the explanation may be difficult. Gravitation is the force which condenses matter ; it would, if unresisted, draw more and more matter together, building globes of great size. Against this, ethereal pressure is the main disruptive force (doubtless assisted by the centrifugal force of the sun's rotation) ; its function is to prevent the accumulation of large masses."

The theories of Einstein lead to the unpic-turable idea of a *finite* universe, and its dimen-sions have been provisionally computed. Its circumference is estimated (very hypothetically, of course) at about 100 million light years, or 600 million million million miles. This is ten times the distance from us to the farthest spiral nebula. The weight of the Einstein world is estimated at 10^{54} grams, or about a hundred trillion times the mass of the sun.

We need not boggle over the question, If the universe is finite, what is beyond ? So might a two-dimensional caterpillar, burrowing in the skin of an orange, say to itself : " If I go

on and on, I *must* come to an end sometime."
We are tri-dimensional caterpillars—all except
some mathematicians, who are quite at home in
the four-dimensional curved world, with Time
and Space interlaced.

THE OUTSKIRTS OF THE GALAXY.

Besides the main galaxy, which we have
compared to a heavenly city and its suburbs,
there are worlds " farther away." There are
peripheral " globular clusters " of stars, and
still farther into the dark country are the non-
galactic spiral nebulæ, which seem to be new
systems in the making. A tiny system like our
solar system impresses us with its extreme
orderliness, but the plan of the universe as a
whole has not been discerned. We must wait
till it is better known. And it must be kept in
mind that, besides the systems that make up the
great galaxy, besides the " globular clusters " of
stars, besides the distant spiral nebulæ, and
besides wandering stars galore, there is the
" dark matter " of the universe. The experts say
that it is probably not of very enormous amount.

THE UNIVERSE : AS IT WAS.

What the astronomers tell us about this is of
much importance in forming a general idea of
Evolution, or, as we prefer to say in this connection, Genesis. But Dr. Herbert Dingle points

out that : " Every avenue back into the past shows a universe sensibly identical with the universe of to-day. There is no record of a different world."

No doubt our sun was once vastly larger before it became the parent of its brood of planets ; no doubt the moon was once born of the earth, or along with it, some say, as a small twin-sister ; no doubt a star passes through a cycle from brilliant giant to dull dwarf, and perhaps the double stars may once have been single ; and so on with other stories. But the point is that even the speculative cosmogonists do not lead us back to any beginning of things. They only lead us back to a state of affairs similar to that which at present exists—an Eternal Now. Our particular system had a genesis from a nebula which has apparently many parallels in the heavens to-day. But the parentage of a nebula is unknown.

THE UNIVERSE : AS IT WILL BE.

According to Dr. Dingle, the distant future is as dim as the distant past. " It is impossible to forecast even the most probable destiny of the universe." No doubt if the universe to-day contains specimens of bodies which are passing through a cycle of changes, we may say that the past of one body will be the future of another.

" Unless some accidental catastrophe should occur, Betelgeuse will be in the next stellar age what Aldebaran is in this."

But if a giant star shrinks and degenerates into a dying dwarf, what becomes of it at last ? We cannot tell, for we do not know of any subsequent post-stellar development that can take place. The dwindling stars are obviously not very informative, since they are too faint to be scrutinised. And the available evidence does not indicate that there is a large number of dark bodies in space. What then becomes of the dead stars ? We do not know.

Perhaps it is unnecessary to suppose that the stars do actually die out. Perhaps they explode before they die, explode into dust and vapour, bringing our thoughts back once more to a diffuse nebula. Perhaps the unkind reader will say that they have been very nebulous all the time.

We rub our eyes, for there is a plough already in the bare harvest field that we have been staring at in our long reverie. " After the last," as Browning said, " returns the first, though a long compass round be fetched." From nebula to nebula, we discern no beginning and no trace of ending. Becoming, being, having been—and becoming again. *Werden und Vergehen, und Weiter-Werden.* That seems to be the scientific picture.

VIII

THE GOSPEL OF EVOLUTION

WE hope that this title—the Gospel of Evolution—will not seem either irreverent or far-fetched, for we mean it very seriously and literally. There *is* good news for man in the story of the Becoming of the system of Living Nature. Perhaps there is better news than has yet been discerned.

WHAT WE OWE TO DARWIN.

Darwin focussed so many ideas that were previously dim, made so many old facts new, and gave us keys to so many doors, that it is a matter of opinion which of his services was greatest. In our " Darwinism and Human Life " (Melrose, London), we have tried to answer this question in detail. First of all, Darwin gave us the picture of " The Web of Life," the linkage of organisms to one another. Nothing lives or dies to itself ; everything is a retainer to something else. A sparrow cannot fall to the ground without sending a throb through a wide circle. There is a correlation of organisms in Nature something like the correlation of organs in our body, "members one of another." Diverse living creatures often stand or fall together.

As we have said elsewhere (" Science Old and New," 1924, p. 429) : Earthworms plough the fields ; the bees and the flowers are hand and glove ; the mistle-thrush plants the mistletoe ; the minnow nurses the mussel ; the water-wagtail helps the sheep-farmer ; and the squirrel may have its share in making the harvest a success. Suppose the glory that was Greece was in part dimmed, as some historians maintain, by the intrusion of malaria ; the disease is sown by mosquitoes, whose larval stages in the water are very effectively checked by minnows. Well may one exclaim : " Ye Gods and little fishes ! " Darwin gave naturalists a fresh vision of the Web of Life.

THE STRUGGLE FOR EXISTENCE.

In the second place we may rank Darwin's realisation of the struggle for existence, in its length and breadth, its height and depth. It is much more than internecine struggle around the platter of subsistence, it includes all the answers-back that living creatures make to surrounding difficulties and limitations. The struggle for existence often rises to an endeavour after well-being.

> For life is not an idle ore,
> But iron dug from central gloom,
> And heated hot with burning fears,
> And dipped in baths of hissing tears,
> And battered by the shocks of doom
> To shape and use.

A struggle between fellows, between foes, between life and callous things—Darwin saw it whole.

A WORLD IN FLUX.

Darwin found naturalists with a fixed world, and he left it fluent. In 1844 he wrote to Hooker : " I am almost convinced . . . that species are not (it is like confessing a murder) immutable." Living creatures are changeful, some quickly, some slowly ; there is organic flux. Darwin gave Biology more clearly than before the vision of variability.

NATURE'S SIFTING.

Then came the theory of Nature's sifting, which many biologists would place as the foremost of Darwin's contributions. Just as the breeder or the gardener gets rid of new departures that he does not want, so the Struggle for Existence sifts and singles, now pruning off and again fostering, and we call its work Natural Selection.

But we must not forget that Darwin made the general idea of Organic Evolution current coin of the intellectual realm. It was not his own idea, for it goes back to the old Greek philosophers, or further back still, but he made it convincing. He made the world think in terms of evolution.

MAN AS CROWN OF CREATION.

Another of Darwin's great services was very unpopular ; it was his disclosure of the descent and ascent of man. For Darwin saw that the evolution idea must include man, who cannot but be solidary with the rest of creation. Darwin pointed to the rock whence man was hewn and to the pit whence he was digged. In other words, he showed that men and tentative men sprang from a stock common to them and to the Anthropoid apes. We should dismiss for ever from our thoughts every idea of man being descended from any living monkeys or apes. Darwin's conclusion was that Hominoids and Anthropoids are collateral branches of a common stem which is, for the most part, still hidden in obscurity.

DARWIN AS A LIBERATOR.

Like Abraham Lincoln, who was born on the same day in the same year—February 12th, 1809—Darwin worked for freedom, though we do not suppose he often thought of himself in that way. He removed great fields of inquiry from the tyranny of authority to the freedom of scientific inquiry.

In his very interesting " Impressions of Great Naturalists " (Scribners, 1924), Professor Henry Fairfield Osborn writes :

" I do not see that Darwin's supreme service to his fellow-men was his demonstration of evolution—man could have lived on quite as happily, and perhaps more morally, under the old notion that he was specially made in the image of his Maker. Darwin's supreme service was that he won for man absolute freedom in the study of the laws of Nature."

This is a very interesting statement on the part of a distinguished evolutionist, and we wish to point out why it does not seem to us quite sound.

In the first place, although Darwin was an Emancipator, there were many others who did valiant service in winning freedom to study the laws of Nature. Secondly, it is not merely freedom to inquire that is important, it is the liberation of spirit that the results of free inquiry bring. Darwin gave men a New World, not less important than Columbus's. He made a great contribution towards the truth, and it is the truth that makes us free.

Third, when Professor Osborn suggests that man would have been quite as happy and perhaps more moral under the old notion that he was specially designed in the image of his Maker, is he not coming perilously near the fallacy of false antithesis in which the fundamentalists flounder. For the idea of being created in the image of God is at heart a *religious* idea, which is not, in its essence, in any way affected by the scientific description of the Ascent of Man. There is no antithesis between being a scion of a stock common to Anthropoids and Hominoids and being a fulfilment of a Divine Purpose. These two statements are in two different languages.

We must not labour our criticism of Professor Osborn's position, which we should not have discussed at all if we did not hold him in the highest admiration ; but we must notice, in conclusion, that when man is in search of a scientific formulation, it is irrelevant to think of its effect on his happiness or morals. If a scientific account of the Becoming of Animate Nature is forthcoming, we cannot hesitate in our acceptance. It is a case of *Floreat veritas ruat cœlum ;* we have no choice. If the conclusion is sound, it must be in the direction of the truth ; and however severe the pains of progress may be, man will be eventually happier and more moral the nearer to the truth he comes.

DARWIN'S SUPREME SERVICE.

If among Darwin's many services we must try to single out the greatest, we should say that he made the general idea of Organic Evolution convincing by beginning to show how the process may have worked. He began to change a *modal* theory of Becoming into a *causal* theory. Many naturalists before Darwin had been evolutionists. Think of Buffon, Lamarck, and Treviranus, to mention only three ; and we should not forget Darwin's grandfather. But none of them stated the case with anything like Darwin's forcefulness, though Spencer's marshalling of the so-called evidence was also masterly. Patiently and in detail, never pressing, never dogmatising, eager to anticipate difficulties, Darwin showed in " The Origin of Species " that a multitude of facts—anatomical, palæontological, embryological, and geographical, besides those of domestication and cultivation—all pointed to the evolutionist conclusion that the present is the natural outcome of a simpler past. Where positive demonstration was impossible, was there ever, in the history of science, such a cumulatively convincing argument ? Yet it was not an induction so much as a multitudinous illustration of the soundness of a deduction —we should rather say, of a discernment.

Yet the essential difference between Darwin's evolutionism and that of his predecessors was not, we think, the massiveness of his " evidence " that evolution was the master-key. It was that he showed how the evolutionary process may have worked. He secured the modal theory by disclosing a reasonable causal theory—more reasonable in the eyes of his contemporaries than the causal theories of, let us say, Lamarck, to select the most noteworthy.

To those who have got beyond polemical argument it would not be upsetting if it should turn out that radical changes were necessary in Darwin's chief causal theory of Evolution, namely, the sifting of new departures by the struggle for existence. Huxley was never very enthusiastic over this Natural Selection theory. Wallace was severely critical of Darwin's Sexual Selection theory ; yet both were convinced evolutionists, and—this is our point—not merely because of Darwin's impressive array of locks that the Evolution master-key fits, but because Darwin disclosed the possibility of arriving at a reasonable scientific causal account of the origin of species.

THE PAGEANT OF LIFE.

The process of organic evolution from invisible animalcules to birds and mammals and man has a magnificence that cannot be exaggerated. It is the sublimest of all spectacles. It has been a process in which the time required has been, so to speak, no consideration. For hundreds of millions of years it has continued without rest or haste. Broad foundations have been laid so that a splendid superstructure has been made secure. In spite of the somewhat puzzling disappearance of many masterpieces, like the Flying Dragons or Pterodactyls, there has been an ascent of life and a remarkable conservation of great gains. Throughout the ages Life has been slowly creeping upwards.

No doubt the process of organic evolution does not move steadily in the direction of that increased intricacy and harmony, which we call "differentiation" and "integration," but *on the whole* there has been something like progress. The tapeworm, in its inglorious life of ease, is a product of evolution as well as the lark at heaven's gate, but the bird is more characteristic of organic evolution than the parasite. Evolution is characteristically integrative.

EVOLUTION NOT ALWAYS PROGRESSIVE.

Let us admit frankly that evolution has not invariably been in the direction which man at his best calls " progress." There are strange blind alleys, for instance, as in sponges, where there is an extraordinary exuberance of sheer complexity and remarkable architectural beauty, and yet no notable advance. For sponges seem to represent a *cul de sac ;* they do not lead on to any other class of animals. They illustrate evolution among themselves, within a relatively short radius, so to speak; but they are not progressive types. There are intelligible reasons for this, which do not concern us here, for instance, in the fact that sponges, after a short free-swimming, larval life, settle down on their mouth. This is obviously a bad start. We admit that evolution is not always progress !

THE GROWING EMANCIPATION OF MIND.

A Flying Dragon or Pterodactyl is undoubtedly a higher creature than a newt in the quag, meaning by " higher " an increase in intricacy (differentiation) and control (integration). Somewhat in the same way, a railway locomotive of 1925 is " higher " than Stephenson's " Puffing Billy," which a cow on the track could stop. No doubt the Flying Dragon was more master of its fate than any newt ; and in this also there is progress. But a scrutiny of evolutionary advance shows something else—a persistent improvement in brains, and that means an increasing emancipation of the Psyche. This is another feature in the Gospel of Evolution. Not only has there been a general advance, there has been emphasis on the advance of mind. We see this more clearly when we compare, not Reptile and Amphibian, but Bird and Reptile.

BRAIN-STRETCHING.

Towards the end of the Cretaceous Period there emerged from an Insectivore stock a race of small, shrew-like arboreal mammals—the primitive Prosimians. They are known only as fossils, and therefore very vaguely ; but they point the way to the Half-monkeys or Lemurs, the Spectral Tarsiers, and the Tree-Shrews. Reading back from their successors, we can form some idea of the promiseful Prosimians.

Consider, for instance, the vivacious tree-shrews (Tupaia), which range from India to Java—clever little creatures of engaging ways and of surpassing interest to the evolutionist. Their significance lies in the reduction of the smell-centres of the brain and the correlated increase of the region into which the other senses pour their tidings, and from which there issue the orders that control agile and precise movements. This was a step in the right direction !

Other hints of progress are to be found in the strange goggle-eyed Spectral Tarsier of Borneo and Java. It is often ranked as one of the Lemurs or Half-Monkeys, but it stands very much by itself. It shows a further reduction of the olfactory region, a further increase in the centres for sight and touch and for motor control. A new area of the anterior cortex of the fore-brain, an area which Professor Elliot Smith calls the " neo-pallium," is beginning to assert itself. This was another step in the right direction.

According to Elliot Smith's thought-provoking " Evolution of Man " (Milford, London, 1924), it was before the close of the Eocene Period, millions of years ago, that one of these Tarsioids " acquired the power of stereoscopic vision and became transformed into a primitive monkey, with a very considerable increase in the size of the brain and an enormous enhancement of the power of skilled movement and of intelligence." This highly important event probably occurred somewhere in the neighbourhood of Central America, and from this cradle there arose a restless stock that migrated across ancient land-bridges and peopled Africa and Europe and Eastern Asia with *monkeys*.

We have already referred to this interesting anatomical story, that a series of brains—tree-shrew, tarsier, marmoset, monkey, ape, and man —shows the gradual reduction of the olfactory region, and the gradual predominance of the centres for vision, hearing, touch, dexterity, attention, and the unifying of the brain. This has been *a great trend of evolution*, an encouraging one for us. Success has been to the visualisers. While we have reason to admire the *general* advance of organisms through hundreds of millions of years, we cannot but be more interested in the gradually increasing dominance of " mind " in the higher reaches of life. By "mind" we mean, not so much think-ing—a human luxury—as *mastery* on the one hand and *good feeling* on the other. The higher animals get more out of life than is possible for the lower ranks. In short, are we not missing one of the largest facts of organic evolution if we fail to see that it means an emergence of lives that are increasingly *satisfactions in themselves*. Here is one of the lessons of evolution for man.

THE WEAVING OF THE WEB OF LIFE.

A vigorous man multiplies his relationships, and this is characteristic of vigorous living crea-tures. They link themselves on to other creatures—sometimes, no doubt, in desperation, but sometimes in a more masterful way. Thus, to be concrete, flowers and insects have become bound up together in mutual dependence and mutual perfecting. The flower is the stronger because the appropriate visiting insect carries the fertilising golden dust from one plant to another of the same kind, and this secures cross-fertilisation, which tends, on the whole, to favour more seed and better seed. No doubt some flowers get on very well with wind-pollination and others with self-pollination, while the eminently successful dandelion has relapsed into parthenogenesis. That is to say, it habitually produces good seed that does not require any fertilisation at all. But after we have made these admissions, the big fact remains that the cross-pollination of flowers is profitable, and is attained in most cases by a linkage between the plants on the one hand and certain insects, like bees, on the other.

But the insects are also strengthened in their struggle for existence by their alliance with plants, which afford valuable condensed food—nectar and pollen—kept in good condition by the sheltering parts of the flower. And it is a very interesting fact that other animals besides insects have discovered the advantage of the flower-visiting habit. Thus recent work has shown that there are about 1,600 flower-birds, mostly in tropical countries, which habitually visit long-tubed blossoms for the sake of the nectar. Humming-birds and sun-birds are good examples, and there is probably more than a spice of awareness in the new relations which they have established.

We have taken a familiar instance of vital linkages in the web of life, and have selected what is, perhaps, the best instance of all, but it is only an example of what is characteristic of living creatures, that they become bound together in mutual dependence. Thus, as John Locke said, every one is a retainer to some other part of Nature. Nothing lives or dies to itself.

EVOLUTION OF SIEVES.

The evolutionary interest of this is twofold. In the struggle for existence a minute new departure can be tested in relation to the web of life in which the creature is implicated. This means, as it were, a fine-meshed sieve. George Meredith said of Nature that she " winnows roughly,"

> " Behold the life of ease, it drifts.
> The sharpened life commands its course ;
> She winnows, winnows roughly, sifts
> To dip her chosen in her source.
> Contention is the vital force
> Whence pluck they brain, her prize of gifts."

But what often impresses us when a variant is tested in reference to its environing inter-relations, is the fineness of the winnowing. To change the metaphor, a nuance may be decisive. The difference between a Shibboleth and a Sibboleth may have " survival value."

THE DANGER OF SLIPPING BACK.

On the whole, as we have seen, life has been slowly creeping upwards through the long ages. If we dare not call it progress, because that word is so deeply coloured with human ideals, then we must get some other very similar word like advancement. But why should there be this persistent advance ? Why are not retrogressions much more common ?

Part of the answer may be found in the insurgent nature of the living creature, its capacity for storing energy, its will to live. There is also a momentum in evolution, for a race gathers volume like money at compound interest and nothing succeeds like success. But may not the web of life be one of the factors that prevent slipping back ? If there is a gradually elaborated external system of inter-relations, these will tend to make it more difficult for organisms to slip down the steep rungs of the ladder.

In the case of flowers and insects, retro-gressive variations on either side will be less likely to take hold just because Nature's sifting will operate in reference to two parties which are intimately bound up together. Suppose the flowering plant varied in the direction of being less odoriferous or less nectariferous, this would automatically handicap it in reference to its habitual insect visitors attracted by fragrance and sweet food. Variants that continued in this direction would tend to be sifted out, though in some cases they might evade elimination by falling back on some other way of being fertilised.

Suppose, on the other hand, that the insect varied in the direction of a dulled sense of smell or a shortened tongue, these variants would tend to be sifted out, since they would not find the fragrant flowers or would not be able to reach the nectary. This is the ordinary Darwinian theory, but our point is that the external inter-relations between living creatures become more and more complex, and must automatically operate against retrogression. If so, there is another lesson for Man from Organic Evolution, namely, that the strengthening and complexifying of inter-relations is one of the ways of *securing progress.*

UNITY OF LIFE.

When we try to envisage the long process of Organic Evolution, what do we see ? We are impressed by the extraordinary manifoldness, as if Nature were an artist with inexhaustible resources ; with the finish of workmanship, for there is nothing scamped, and a feather may be the outcome of a million years of experimenting. There is all-pervasive beauty, though half of it is born to blush unseen. There is an insurgence of life, that fills every corner, and a plasticity of life that seizes every niche of opportunity. And we have spoken of the general progressiveness through the long ages.

But there is another large fact—the unity of the process. It is not merely that the touch of protoplasm makes the whole world kin, and that the same fundamental activities find expression from amœba to man. It is not merely that the same prism serves throughout to analyse the light of life, its three sides being the living creature, its activity, and its surroundings—Organism, Function, Environment. It is not merely that we see throughout, in a hundred forms, the same logical process—*the sifting and singling of heritable variations*. What more is there ?

There is *the unity of the tree of life*. The Animal Kingdom is a vast system of blood-relationships. Its branches feel their way towards all the points of the compass, as in a tree growing freely in a spacious place ; some point up and others down ; some are straight-limbed and others are gnarled ; but there is the same sap in them all. What we have to deal with is a genealogical tree. No one would dream of suggesting that insects or molluscs, for instance, were on the direct line leading to the backboned animals, for the great classes diverge in directions of their own from a main stem of generalised creatures that is but vaguely known, yet it is very interesting to find what one might call a " conservatism in evolution." When an effective substance or structure has been reached, it is not let go. Thus hæmoglobin, the reddish pigment of the blood, which is invaluable for its oxygen-capturing powers, makes its first appearance in the relatively simple worms called Nemerteans. They may, perhaps, get the credit of its invention. Now there are many animals higher in the scale than Nemerteans which have not got hæmoglobin, yet it has never been lost sight of, so to speak. Unless we suppose that it was evolved independently more than once, it must have been firmly conserved along many lines. It is not present in some of the pioneer backboned animals, such as sea-squirts and lance-lets, yet it is never absent from Frogs to Man.

CONSERVATISM IN EVOLUTION.

A peculiar kind of " tank-like " rolling movement is seen in many of the simplest animals, such as the common Amœbæ. For this reason it is called " amœboid." It is a peculiarly effective kind of protoplasmic movement; and our point is that it is continued on to the top of the tree. Most "bodied" animals, except thread-worms and lancelets, have among their other kinds of cells amœboid "phagocytes," which serve many useful purposes in the body, and they, though part and parcel of the tissues of their possessors, are the counterparts of the aboriginal Amœbæ. The same movement is to be seen in all white blood corpuscles, and when the nerve-cell in a developing embryo sends its fine thread growing out into the surrounding tissue.

Or, once more, there appear in earthworms and their allies in the sea numerous twisted, thread-like tubes, called nephridia, which serve for the filtering of nitrogenous waste from the blood. These minute kidney-tubes are very effective structures, and, to speak metaphorically, the evolving Proteus keeps a firm hold on them. There are over ninety pairs of them in the pioneer Vertebrate known as the lancelet, and they form the foundation of the kidneys in all backboned animals. There is a conservatism in evolution.

BALANCED PROGRESS.

The process of Organic Evolution reveals a *balanced* progress. The whole world of organisms forms a coherent system which has moved to some extent as a whole. No doubt there were jolts and disharmonies, which are marked, for instance, by the disappearance of entire races of animals and plants, including many masterpieces, yet the general fact is the balanced advance of an increasingly coherent system.

It is too simple to say that there are fishes in the sea *in order that* there may be a livelihood for fishermen. It is too simple to say that there are countless multitudes of minute crustaceans in the sea *in order that* there may be food for fishes. Yet we may say that the multitudes of crustaceans have made the multitudes of fishes possible. Broad foundations have been laid which made further advances possible and stable.

TOP OF THE TREE.

No evolutionist likes to speak of an *end*. It comes perilously near a contradiction in terms ; for evolution is going on. Thus, though man is the present crown of creation, we hope that it is a still-evolving crown. It is quite conceivable that there may be arising, all unbeknownst in our midst, a mutant type which will evolve beyond the modern man as far as he has evolved beyond his distant cousin, the man of Neanderthal.

But our present point is that man is at the top of a stately genealogical tree, with which he is continuous. If he is solidary with the rest of creation it seems legitimate to look at the process in the light of its resultant. Men of science, for whom the term " Scient " has been suggested, often object to this, maintaining that it is a philosophical, not a scientific, procedure. But is this not pedantically methodological? The embryologist always looks at the developing embryo in the light of the adult.

Whether it be scientific or not, it seems to us to be good sense to try to envisage the long groaning and travailing of creation in the light of its outcome in man. The evolutionist conclusion must be accepted as the inferential scientific description of what actually occurred in the irrecoverable past, but we are trying to suggest some reasons why this scientific conclusion should be *welcome*. And one of these reasons is that it gives the world unity when we recognise man as the crown of Nature, the coping-stone (for the time being) of the stately edifice which has so slowly risen. *Nature became articulate and self-conscious in Man.*

If man is descended from, or has ascended
from, an ancient stock common to him and to
the anthropoid apes, we can better understand
that there should be some coarse threads in his
nature. As Shakespeare said, the web of our
life is of mingled yarn, good and ill together.
Just as there are anachronisms in man's body, so
in his personality. There are deep-rooted
impulses and strange vagaries that bear the
mark of the beast. As every man knows, we
have to let " the ape and tiger die." Even in
the commonplace details of life, it is safer not
to awaken " sleeping dogs," if we can help it.
Some of these primitive pre-dispositions, older
than Homo, form part of what is now called the
Primary Unconscious. Perhaps one of these is
the deeply-rooted and very widespread repulsion
to snakes.

In thinking of these troublesome legacies, we
must in fairness recognise that they come to us
down the ages along with a much larger endowment of good qualities. There are tares in our
field, but there is much more wheat. We have
courage and gentleness, patience and strength to
endure, and much more to be grateful for. Even
the ape and the tiger must not be denied their
good points.

More deeply, however, it should be recognised that we do not inherit in piecemeal fashion ; we inherit the characters of *Homo sapiens*, a new creature, a unified emergence, although not without his encumbrances. The poet spoke graphically of himself as " stuccoed all over with quadrupeds," but that is not quite accurate psycho-biology. The organism is a unity. Some of the threads in our personality are coarser than others, thus we cannot sneer without showing the dog's tooth, as Darwin pointed out. Yet even these threads have been humanised in the course of evolution.

FOR MAN'S ENCOURAGEMENT?

Since Man is the long result of time, since his inheritance is the outcome of pre-human ages of " testing all things and holding fast that which is good," it would be a real encouragement to know that his face was hereditarily set in the right direction. Is there something in him that can be regarded as making for progress ? Has he any heritable momentum towards the highest values—the good, the beautiful, and the true ? To some this will seem a preposterous question, and others may think that it has already been rightly answered in the negative by the clear-headed Huxley.

HUXLEY'S PICTURE.

" In the case of mankind, the self-assertion,

the unscrupulous seizing upon all that can be grasped, the tenacious holding of all that can be kept, which constitute the essence of the struggle for existence, have answered. For his successful progress, as far as the savage state, man has been largely indebted to those qualities which he shares with the ape and the tiger ; his exceptional physical organisation, his sociability, his curiosity, and imitativeness, his ruthless and ferocious destructiveness when his anger is roused by opposition."

There is much truth in this picture, and yet it is blotched by its onesidedness. Primitive man must have been endowed with robust qualities. As we have said elsewhere : " Primitive man was not as strong as a lion or a gorilla, but he was no weakling. He was no acquiescent person, but insurgent. He was living too dangerously to be meek and mild. His loins were girt—metaphorically, at least—and his lamp was lit. He was self-assertive and a hustler " (" What is Man ? " Methuen, London, 1924, p. 46).

So far we agree with Huxley's picture. But when we think of the helplessness of the human infant, of its prolonged infancy and childhood, we feel the survival-value of gentleness. When we think of the relative weakness of the individual man, or, for that matter, of the single

206

family, we feel the survival-value of mutual aid and self-subordination. Huxley, indeed, admitted the importance of sociability, but the emphasis of his picture was on individualistic qualities ; our proposition is that had these been dominant, primitive man would not have survived at all.

HUXLEY'S ADVICE.

There was always a sharp point and a shrewd thrust in Huxley's deliverances, but, like most good fighters, he often stated a case in terms that were extreme. Thus, not being a field-naturalist, he painted a picture of the struggle for existence which was far too red. He saw the " gladiatorial show," the " dismal cockpit," the " Hobbesian war " of each against all, but he did not see so clearly the mutual aid, the kin-sympathy, the parental sacrifice, the self-subordination within the animal community. So it appeared to Huxley that ethical progress for man depends upon his combating the cosmic process, *solus contra mundum*. Instead of *following Nature*, it was man's task in his ethical endeavours to reverse her methods.

EVOLUTIONARY OPTIMISM.

Our thesis is very different from Huxley's—suspiciously different, we sometimes think ! We regard man as the outcome of certain great trends in evolution which are congruent with the " higher values," which men at their best have always held to be best, which are, in any case, *given health and wealth*, the greatest satisfactions in themselves—the good and the doing of it, the beautiful and the making of it, the true and the seeking after it.

Man is the highest mammal, but the very word suggests mothering ; and while the success of mammals is undoubtedly due in part to their teeth and claws, their eyes and brains, and so on, it is also due to the maternal care and the parental tutelage. Mammals have succeeded in no small degree *because they are good*. There has been persistent selection along the line of good lovers and good parents ; and man, being an outcome of that line, has in his very blood a momentum towards morality.

OMNIPRESENT BEAUTY.

There is easy beauty, like a peacock's tail, and there is difficult beauty, like a serpent on the rock, but almost all through the world of life there is beauty. What exceptions are there ? Many domesticated animals and cultivated plants are far from beautiful, but they are not " natural products." They bear the marks of man's clumsy fingers and bear witness to the shortsightedness of his desires. Many half-made embryonic and larval creatures are not very beautiful, though others are masterpieces from start to finish. " Ugly is only half-way to a thing," Meredith said, and we are not surprised that some stages in the making of an animal are not beautiful. It is of interest to remember how carefully many of them are hidden away !

Diseased and crippled creatures are often repulsive, but these are exceedingly unusual in Wild Nature. The exceptions that may rise in the mind are probably due to human interference. Nature is all for health, if one may indulge in harmless personification, and one of the hall-marks of health is beauty. When the physician speaks of a " beautiful tumour " or " a beautiful case of confluent smallpox," he is obviously using the word in a professional and peculiar sense. We mean by the beautiful that which excites the æsthetic emotion. " A thing of beauty is a joy for ever."

A third exception must be made for parasites, for many of them, though beautiful in detail, are very ugly. Perhaps this is just because they are " drifters " that have jettisoned independence. They bear in their ugliness the stigma of dishonour.

Our thesis is, that apart from domestication and cultivation, apart from the half-finished, the diseased, and the parasitic, all living creatures are artistic harmonies, things of beauty. Their beauty is, in part, the expression of orderly and harmonious living, in part the outcome of long sifting which has removed all structural incongruity and functional discord, and in part the Psyche shining through the flesh. It is an outcome of Organic Evolution ; and its momentum is resident in man just because of his solidarity with the rest of creation. Here also there is encouragement.

A PREMIUM ON BRAINS.

We recognise in Organic Evolution a trend towards the raw materials of morality and another trend towards beauty, but how can we expect to find anything congruent with truth and the search for it ? Yet one of the big facts of Organic Evolution is the gradual emergence of the mental aspect of behaviour. There is a premium on clear-headedness and a reward to the finer emotions. Nature, as we have said, is all for health, and with the health of the body goes the health of the mind. The healthy animals have clear eyes and nimble brains. They know their region, they solve problems, they have words to converse with, they make experiments. Is not the highest expression of the healthy mind just the search after truth ?

THE MOMENTUM OF EVOLUTION WITH MAN AT HIS BEST.

Thus we reach what is, at any rate, an interesting conclusion, that there are in Organic Evolution three great trends which are congruent with man's highest ideals of the good, the beautiful, and the true. And it is not merely that these trends have been, and still are, influential in Wild Nature, we mean also that they are, in a real sense, continued into man's being, bred in the bone and embued in the blood. We venture to think that Huxley was in error when he concluded that " the cosmic process has no sort of relation to moral ends." We are nearer the position of Professor Patrick Geddes, who has spoken of Nature as a " materialised ethical process," meaning mainly that some of the greatest steps in organic progress, the rise of mammals for instance, are in part due to subordinations of the nutritive and self-regarding to the reproductive and species-regarding activities.

If this is sound it is an important part of the Gospel of Evolution. Our affiliation with the beasts helps to bring us on to the side of the angels.

PRINTED IN GREAT BRITAIN BY THE WHITEFRIARS PRESS, LTD., LONDON AND TONBRIDGE